SEX SOUL AND ISLAM

SEX SOUL AND ISLAM

OSMAN SIDEK
ENON MANSOR

CLARITAS
BOOKS

1 2 3 4 5 6 7 8 9 10

CLARITAS BOOKS

Bernard Street, Swansea, United Kingdom
Milpitas, California, United States

CLARITAS
BOOKS

First Published in September 2022

Typeset in Acumin Concept 14/9

Sex, Soul and Islam
By Osman Sidek and Enon Mansor

A CIP catalogue record for this book is available from the British Library

ISBN: 978-1-80011-987-1

The pleasure that is felt in sexual intercourse
between a man and his wife is a little sign of the
next-worldly pleasure.

IMAM GHAZALI

ABOUT THE AUTHORS

We are a husband and wife writing team. We met in university and married after graduation. Soon after, we both began working as trainers in marriage preparation courses conducted by the Muslim Converts' Association Singapore (MCAS), the Islamic Religious Council Singapore (MUIS) and Singapore's then Ministry of Community Development, Youth and Sports (MCYS). In 1998, we co-wrote *Tranquil Hearts – A Guide to Marriage*, which was co-published by MCAS and MUIS and is still being used as the textbook for the marriage preparation programme in MCAS. In 2011, we collaborated with an Islamic scholar and a social worker to design and conduct *Suara Kekasih*, a series of sexual enrichment workshops for married couples in Malay. And in 2021, we conducted an online seminar hosted by the Institute of Islamic Development and Research, UK and attended by about 300 participants worldwide.

Enon Mansor graduated from the National University of Singapore (NUS) with a BA in Sociology in 1988 and a BA (1987) and MA in Social Work (2003), giving her a strong academic foundation in studying marriage as a sociological phenomenon. After the publication of *Tranquil Hearts*, she was actively involved in the standardisation of the syllabi for marriage preparation courses undertaken by MCAS and MUIS. Enon Mansor has more than thirty years of professional experience as a researcher, writer, social worker and marriage counsellor – helping hundreds of couples reconcile, rejuvenate and strengthen their marriages as well as separate harmoniously.

As an activist teacher, **Osman Sidek** taught introductory Islamic knowledge and marriage preparation to new and non-Muslims in the 90s. This exposure honed his skills in presenting Islam and marriage to a discerning adult audience from diverse cultural backgrounds. As an offshoot of the *Suara Kekasih* sexual enrichment programme, he wrote articles for *Sutra* magazine (Singapore) on sexual issues and co-counselled with Enon on a number of sex-related marital dysfunction cases for the *Syariah* Court's Marriage Counselling Program.

This book is chiefly researched and written by Osman with academic direction, critical input and clinical insights from Enon. All the case examples we mention in the book are real, with the majority of them taken from Enon's professional counselling experience, but for brevity and flow as well as client privacy, the cases have been summarised into broad strokes of relevant key points and referred to collectively as ours. Check out the authors' website: **www.enonandosman.com**

ACKNOWLEDGEMENTS

Sex, Soul and Islam has benefitted immensely from a heavily critical review of earlier manuscripts by possibly the most Western thinking friend we have, David Hanif Coulson. Augmented by comments from his wife Hanin Hussain and their son Deen Coulson, David's review was a valuable voice from outside our echo chamber. As a result, many Islamic concepts, rulings, norms and the likes that we took for granted had to be substantiated. We believe this process made the book a lot more relatable to its target audience who are likely to be equally questioning and critical of established Muslim ideas.

From the other end of the cultural spectrum, the book equally benefited from Azhar-educated Ustaz Mohamad Khair Rahmat's comments and advice. We thank him for spending his valuable time reading our entire manuscript to seek out any views which are outrightly un-Islamic or potentially contentious. In addition, he kindly verified the authenticity of all the hadiths used in this book, identified the fabricated narrations to be discarded and highlighted the weak narrations which we used with qualifications on three occasions. We thank Ustaz Khair and David equally for keeping our views well-balanced between orthodoxy and modernity.

Last but not least, we thank Claritas Books for their temerity in advancing this potentially controversial view on a definitely sensitive topic by a relatively unknown writing team to a global readership. In view of the hundreds of unsolicited book proposals he must have received, we are immensely grateful that Wali-ur Rahman did not throw ours into his recycling bin. Then there was Shaykh Sharif H. Banna whose incisive review of the manuscript was instrumental in addressing argumentation loopholes and inadequacies at critical junctures of the book. We are grateful to him.

CONTENTS

PREFACE
WHY THIS BOOK?

In the Name of Allah, Most Gracious, Most Merciful

If internet discussions are anything to go by, Islam must seem like a very strange religion to many in terms of its laws, norms and practices. No less among these is how sex is treated in Islam – popular portrayals of which make great sound bites and media headlines. For example, news stories portraying the *hudud* (punishments) on fornication as draconian, the hijab as oppressive, conjugal rights as male-serving and wife-beating and marital rape being par for the course among Muslims. Sexually speaking, this religion must seem to the world at large like a real killjoy, especially for its female adherents.

There are, of course, plenty of non-Muslims who read between the headlines and take popular portrayals of Islam in art, literature and entertainment with a liberal pinch of salt, instead of judging us based on superficialities. Our concern, however, is its effect on fellow Muslims and whether such routine exposure to negative stereotypes surreptitiously instils a subliminal sense that Islamic sexual mores are indeed rather strange when judged by the global mainstream standard. We note this in light of Muslim quarters calling for liberal reinterpretations of classical laws so that Islam can align with modern values while others indulge in literal and unquestioning implementation of such laws as an expression of piety. Never mind the detractors, these two extremes within our own communities are enough to complicate our understanding of what Islam actually says about sex.

In response, many websites have emerged correcting misconceptions perpetrated by those whose agenda is to show Islam in a bad light as well as answering genuine inquiries over specific sex-related laws, rulings and every day practicalities. Hoping to contribute towards this reclamation of the sexual in Islam, this book offers a comprehensive look at what Islam really says about sex, but not in the "all you need to know" sense. Rather, it is about understanding where sex lies in the holistic message of Islam – in its theories, practice and embodiment in the Muslim person.

As such, the range of issues, questions, laws and etiquettes discussed in this book is not exhaustive, nor is it organised systematically as *Sex, Soul and Islam* is not meant to be encyclopaedic or instructive in nature. Instead, we hope it provides an opportunity for reflection for fellow Muslims wanting to understand why their long-held sexual laws and values are what they are and to discover new meanings and understandings in those laws. We offer these reflections from the viewpoint of marriage educators and marital counsellors who have counselled many couples whose negative sexual relationships have had a profound impact on their marriage and vice versa. Our experiences have convinced us that a well-rounded under-standing and observance of the philosophical, legal and relational dimensions of sexual teachings in Islam is extremely important for Muslim marriages.

To begin with, you may notice that the mainstream narrative on sex in Islam centres largely around its laws including rules, regulations, *halal-haram* and punishments – with *hudud* as the favoured lightning rod. Much of the outside world knows Islam through this prism, using a much maligned and misunder-stood word, *sharia,* as the embodiment of Islam's rigidity and repression. Yet, this view of Islam is also prevalent even among Muslims, including in how their marriages and sexual relationships are conducted.

However, *sharia* as Islamic law defines proper behaviour, constitutes only one aspect of Islamic guidance. Islam's belief system clarifies the meaning of life and is its solid foundation while its moral precepts, embodying both belief and conduct of the believer, completes it. As a whole, the aspects of faith, law and morality in-terweave into one comprehensive framework of guidance. An inordinate obsession with legality does injustice to any subject if it is to be understood from an Islamic perspective. As such, this book looks at the sexual connection to Islamic faith, law and morality, in four chapters as follows:

Chapter One: The Element of Sex in Our Faith investigates where, how and why sex figures in the Islamic worldview of existence. This connection between sex and belief explains why sex is treated the way it is in Islam. Inevitably, this leads to marriage, the institution through which the sexual experience helps mankind internalise, manifest and embody that very worldview of existence.

Chapter Two: What's the Deal with Conjugal Rights investigates whether the sexual ideals envisaged in Islam's belief system and intended by its laws have been fulfilled in Muslim societies. The findings highlight the need for a re-understanding of conjugal rights which transcends upholding individual rights to sex with a view towards embracing mutual bliss in lovemaking. This conceptual reframing would reconnect the legal with the relational aspects of sexual guidance as found in Islamic teachings.

Chapter Three: Rulings and Etiquettes of Sex. If Chapter Two rekindles the spirit of the law, this chapter illustrates how the letter of the law deals with the classically discussed sexual issues to the latest new-fangled trends, fetishes and genres of sexual practice. It binds us to solid Islamic values as we learn from multiple sources of sexual knowledge to enrich our experiences.

Chapter Four: The Sexual Experience starts from where Chapter Two left off, by first establishing that like many other ideals behind Islamic practices, the ideal sexual experience ultimately requires a hands-on, continual, life-long process of nurturing between lovers. This is the purview of character refinement, where a healthy interpersonal relationship is one of its major focus. A hadith which differentiates human lovemaking from animal mating becomes the basis of a lifetime of mutual care and support throughout a marriage, beginning with the first night, through to mid-marriage and meno-andropause.

The Epilogue summarises our reflections with a story of an unlikely alliance between the carnal and spiritual dimensions of the human experience in the soul's journey through life on Earth and beyond.

Osman Sidek
Enon Mansor

Culture is not genetically predetermined; it is
non-instinctive. It is the result of social invention
and is transmitted and maintained solely through
communication and learning.

E. ADAMSON HOEBEL

Chapter 1
The Element of Sex in Our Faith

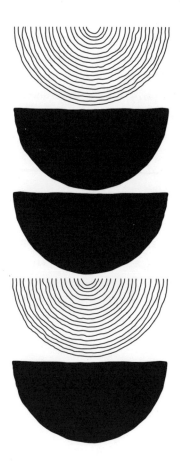

Brief Overview of Islam

Islam calls itself a *'deen'* or a 'way of life' that encompasses every aspect of the believer's time on this Earth. For Muslims, it is the promised guidance, emanating directly from the Creator:

> We said, "Go down from it, all of you. And when guidance comes to you from Me, whoever follows My guidance - there will be no fear concerning them, nor will they grieve.
>
> (Al-Baqarah 2:38)

The message addresses the human mind, body and soul concerning matters of thought, action and values. The totality of which is classified by our scholars into three corresponding branches of knowledge known as *aqidah* (belief system), *sharia* (implementable instructions) and *akhlaq* (moral formation).

Muslims trace back all subjects of human knowledge to this framework in order to understand their respective purpose, permissibility, importance and meaning. Some subjects may pertain to one or two of these branches while others may be inseparably intertwined in that triangulation. The subject of sex – why it exists, how it should be handled and its formative value to our humanity – is one which is intertwined with all three aspects of Islam.

> This day I have perfected for you your religion and completed My favour upon you and have approved for you Islam as religion.
>
> (Al-Ma'idah 5:3)

The word "Islam" is inflected from the words *salam* (peace) and *aslama* (to submit). It is a way of life that calls for submission to the Creator to achieve peace with one's self, with society and with the Creator Himself. The word Muslim refers to a person who submits thus. The Islamic belief system, its implementable rules and moral formation collectively clarify the way in which this peace can be reached and its embodiment in the personality of the believer.

Introduction to Islamic Faith

The rudiments of Islamic faith were summarised in a public discourse between the angel Jibrail 🕊, disguised as a man and the Prophet Muhammad 🕊:

> He (Jibrail 🕊) said, "Tell me about iman." (The Prophet 🕊) said, "That you affirm Allah 🕊, His angels, His Books, His messengers, and the Last

Day, and that you affirm the Decree, the good of it and the bad of it." He
said, "You have told the truth."

(Nawawi)

The word *iman* is generally translated as faith and the six articles mentioned in the hadith above are known as the articles of faith. As a whole, they explain the origin, purpose and destination of life on Earth. Our existence in this Universe is a conscious product of a Perfect Being, Allah ﷻ. Life's purpose is made known to human beings through His spiritual servants (angels), human agents (messengers), and ad-verbatim revelations (Books). Through the agency of these three articles, the purpose and nature of our being is revealed in the subjects called "the Last Day" and "the Decree".

"The Last Day", also known as the Day of Judgment, explains that life on Earth is a temporary period of preparation for everlasting life in the Hereafter. This opportunity comes to mankind in the form of his God-given role as a vicegerent, namely to establish the well-being of the Earth and its inhabitants. Conscientious Muslims strive to find their own role in life and fulfil it to best of their ability.

And [mention, O Muhammad], when your Lord said to the angels, "Indeed, I will
make upon the earth a successive authority."... And We said, "Go down, [all of you]
... you will have upon the Earth a place of settlement and provision for a time."
(Al-Baqarah 2:30 ... 36)

If that is life's purpose, "the Decree", also known as the predestination of events, is a sobering reminder to the vicegerent that despite his foremost position in the hierarchy of creatures, there are bigger creations and grander events that behave and unfold according to God's plans beyond humankind's control and foresight. It is through these events – both the good and the bad – that the character of a man or woman is tested and developed. Their faith in "the Decree" allows them to focus on their duties while entrusting the outcome to Allah ﷻ, knowing that it is their efforts and not the results that they yield that will better them.

And it is He who has made you successors upon the earth and has raised some of
you above others in degrees [of rank] that He may try you through what He has given
you. Indeed, your Lord is swift in penalty; but indeed, He is Forgiving and Merciful.
(Al-An'am 6:165)

Taken as a whole, the six articles constitute a Muslim's worldview. They may study each of the articles in depth to enhance their understanding of life. Yet, the articles alone do not complete this worldview. As the believer learns of creatures, events and experiences beyond the six, they investigate their connection to that narrative of existence which in turn forms their attitude towards them and determines how they treat them. For example, the Muslim may ponder over the reason behind the existence of *jinns* or why some people are born into more wealth than others. It is through such lines of inquiry that we question why sex exists in the first place, which explains our attitude towards it and why we treat it the way we do in Islam.

Sex in the Scheme of Existence

The sexual union between men and women is always presented in a positive light in the Holy Quran. There is no trace of shaming, guilt-tripping or vilification of the animality of "mates of like nature", "mates from among yourselves", or "male and female" in these verses:

> *It is He who created you from one soul and created from it its mate that he might dwell in security with her...*
> (Al-A'raf 7:189)

> *And of His signs is that He created for you from yourselves mates that you may find tranquillity in them; and He placed between you love and mercy. Indeed in that are signs for a people who give thought.*
> (Al-Rum 30:21)

> *And that He creates the two mates - the male and female.*
> (Al-Najm 53:45)

> *And of all things We created two mates; perhaps you will remember.*
> (Al-Dhariyat 51:49)

We take them all as manifestations of "parity" found in the bigger scheme of creation as revealed in that last verse. In the animal sense, this refers to the sexual union between the male and the female *(Al-Najm 53:45)* wherefrom new generations emerge, as the case is with humans:

> *O mankind, fear your Lord, who created you from one soul and created from it its mate and dispersed from both of them many men and women...*
> (Al-Nisa 4:1)

SEX, SOUL AND ISLAM

The word **"Islam"** is inflected from the words *salam* (peace) and *aslama* (to submit). It is a way of life that calls for **submission to the Creator** to achieve **peace** with one's self, with society and with the Creator Himself.

So, as the vicegerent is placed on Earth, sex is the means by which the multitude of souls are accommodated on Earth with the sustained production of human bodies as receptacles that interface with the material Earth. We note this parity as a basis of perpetual Creation. Opposites in the form of "pairs – male and female" (Al-Najm 53:45) attract and their union produces the offspring who will perpetuate the process.

Yet, the opposites bring different qualities, enriching their union sometimes beyond the sum of their qualities. Then, as opposites replicate creation, their offspring stand an enhanced chance of survival and growth under their enriched union. The coming together of man and woman is a union initiated, enhanced and perpetuated by the synergy of opposites displaying the beauty of parity as a creative concept. Repeated throughout the Quran, it is as if these verses are urging humans to indulge their sexual instincts, although the Quran makes it clear that believers must reserve that indulgence exclusively for their spouse.

Certainly, will the believers have succeeded: ... And they who guard their private parts, except from their wives...
(Al-Mu'minun 23:1 ... 5, 6)

Sexual Indulgence or Sexual Repression

Despite the positive associations of sex painted in the Quran, Islam is often depicted as sexually repressive in the media and popular culture. Cliched portrayals of segregation in worship, eschewal of human forms in Islamic art, the *hijab* and capital punishment for sexual crimes all work to compound this severe image. Furthermore, there are many instances of those within our communities who either mistakenly or deliberately abuse aspects of Islamic sexual law, often in ways that are particularly disadvantageous to Muslim women.

In reality, Islam celebrates sex as a meritorious religious act and celibacy and sexual repression are frowned upon. Muslim scholars of the past dealt with the subject frankly and openly and there are many hadiths which record sexual issues being addressed directly by the Prophet ﷺ himself. Even in the present day, online religious advice covers the most intimate of matters ranging from masturbation through to oral sex. Muslims who are properly versed in the Islamic ways would hardly see themselves as sexually repressed.

These very conflicting images of sex in Islam are, in fact, two sides of the same coin. They may appear conflicting when viewed in isolation, but when viewed comprehensively, an objective observer will see that Islam celebrates sex without allowing it to corrupt human behaviour.

It is true that Islam demands from its believers an austere, no-nonsense restraint of their sexual drives through its laws, behavioural codes and practices. As a result, a conscientious believer will approach sex with a higher moral code than any other basic human need. Islam does not cheapen sex by allowing indiscriminate access to it, demean it by publicly exhibiting it and trivialise it through explicit depictions of it. This restraint is what the uninitiated may misconstrue as repression.

The juxtaposition of sexual austerity with its indulgence highlights the status of sex as a protected creation of God. Not to be abused, exploited and demeaned, but to be yearned for with reverence, not voracity. Consequently, it is to be cherished with a sworn commitment to its responsibilities This commitment is not left to individual couples to establish on their own. Instead, it is enshrined in the social institution of marriage,[1] where roles and responsibilities are pre-understood and means of redress for shortcomings and violations are protected and enforceable by society. Hence, marriage becomes an exclusive zone within which the pleasures of sex are indulged in responsibly.

Detractors might contend that sexual austerity cannot beget sexual indulgence even in licensed conditions, given that the conscientious Muslim is deprived of experimenting with different partners outside marriage in order to hone the skills and techniques supposedly necessary for good sex. In Chapter Four, we use modern scientific findings and prophetic wisdom alike to highlight other considerations that are more important for a transcendental sexual experience than factors such as skills, techniques, gadgets, multiple partners and physical endowment. First, though, we will look at the necessity for the exclusive zone or the licence for sex viz-a-viz our worldview of life.

Exclusive Zone of Sexual Indulgence

The necessity for exclusive sexual zones in Islam is not born out of the belief that the sexual instinct is lowly or demeaning, but rather the understanding that the reservation of this enjoyment to the marital context balances the human being's biological need to grow the species with the soul's need for nurture. So, while we give our primal instincts their due respect, we must also note the limit to which we share these with the animal world. We savour the pleasures of animalistic impulses only because it makes sense to do so for the growth of the human body and the continued survival of humankind, but the body is only an outer layer of humanity in which resides its inner being – the soul – and the growth of the soul is a completely different matter.

When a human being is placed on Earth, they are in a perfect state of belief in God. This is revealed by the verse below:

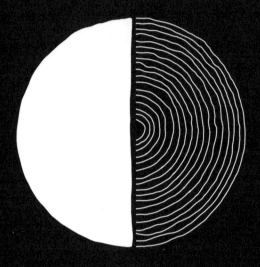

The **sexual union** between men and women is always presented in a **positive light** in the Holy Quran. There is **no** trace of **shaming**, guilt-tripping or vilification of the **animality** of "mates of like nature".

And [mention] when your Lord took from the children of Adam - from their loins
- their descendants and made them testify of themselves, [saying to them], "Am I
not your Lord?" They said, "Yes, we have testified." [This] - lest you should say on
the day of Resurrection, "Indeed, we were of this unaware."
(Al-A'raf 7:172)

Except that after their placement on earth, the choice of whether to accept or reject their true nature is left solely to the human being:

And say, "The truth is from your Lord, so whoever wills - let him believe; and
whoever wills - let him disbelieve."
(Al-Kahf 18:29)

This is in keeping with God's fashioning of mankind as a unique creation who believes, obeys and loves God purely out of their own conviction and not through His design – unlike all other material creatures on Earth. In the following hadith, the Prophet ﷺ confirms this idea while acknowledging the socio-environmental factors that may also influence a person's choices, "There is none born but is created to his true nature (*fitrah*). It is his parents who make him a Jew or a Christian or a Magian ..." (Muslim). In anthropological parlance this refers to the formation of culture in human societies throughout history:

> *Culture is the system of learned behaviour patterns which are*
> *characteristic of the members of a society and which are not the result*
> *of biological inheritance. Culture is not genetically predetermined; it is*
> *non-instinctive. It is the result of social invention and is transmitted and*
> *maintained solely through communication and learning.*
> (E. Adamson Hoebel, et al.)[2]

In Islam, it refers to the formation of *akhlaq* or the individual disposition of a person which leads to the collective culture of their society. In this process, the soul relies on the human mind, senses, emotions and imagination to learn from those around it as well as from those who have preceded it. While anthropology may characterise the past discoveries which influence us as purely "social invention", from an Islamic perspective, they also involve knowledge, ideas, values and virtues which were not human invention but were instead revealed to prophets ﷺ by the Creator. However, the field of anthropology in both Muslim and non-Muslim discourse recognises that the formation of individual disposition and collective culture of mankind are not biologically inherited like animalistic instincts are, but are learnt and hence need a framework of guidance.

The necessity of exclusive zones is down to the fact that the needs for growth of the body and the soul differ diametrically in many crucial ways. For example, the biological need to multiply and perpetuate the species is counter-conducive to the cultivation of values needed for the growth of souls. Multiple and transient sexual partnering which is biologically advantageous to the spreading of genes, does not engender positive emotions like affection, longing, care, compassion or tenderness for enduring relationships to blossom from sexual unions. Instead, the constant changing of partners is more likely to sour relations and evoke negative feelings of hatred, jealousy, rivalry and neglect. Furthermore, it leads to boundless proliferation of offspring resulting in reduced attention from the procreating adults and their neglect of the intergenerational nurturing which is characteristically necessary for human upbringing.

The importance of emotional and psychological bonding (between human lovers and between parents and children) for the cultivation of values means that Islam requires an exclusive nurturing environment to be established before the benefits of sexual indulgence can be enjoyed. It is mainly because of this and the fact that the soul's journey is more important than that of the body, that the existentially crucial sexual instincts are subordinated by the intangible need for an environment conducive to an upbringing within the faith. Interestingly, the need to subordinate the ever-present impulses of the flesh in order to develop the human character is one that is recognised by societies throughout the world and throughout history.

> The prolonged dependence of the human individual on adult
> nurture, character shaping, and cultural transmission, tied in with the
> peculiarities of the relation within the conjugal-natal family, which is the
> nearly universal form in all human societies, makes the untrammelled
> expression of sexuality socially impossible.
>
> (E. Adamson Hoebel, et al.)[3]

Besides, an exclusive sexual partnership can actually be a boon rather than a bane to sexual indulgence. While multiple partnering may seem sexually exciting, the reality is more problematic. Sex inevitably exposes the most private and intimate of physical and emotional shortcomings. Consequently, the daunting prospect of this exposure to another can cause the type of anxiety and insecurity which seriously impedes the full-hearted enjoyment of sex – especially with someone whose commitment to the relationship is yet unproven. However, if a pact exists between the

SEX, SOUL AND ISLAM

two lovers to commit to each other despite any perceived shortcomings and remedy them together, both parties will feel freer to explore, experiment and communicate, creating a safe space in which they can discover what is exciting, enjoyable and satisfying for them.

The formation of exclusive zones between lovers is not left to chance in Islam. Instead, Islam advocates it through the contract of marriage. It is essentially a binding vow between a man and woman witnessed by society and by Allah ﷻ. The rights and obligations of both husband and wife are clearly laid out, ensuring both parties understand what is expected of them and how they should conduct themselves. The conditions and privileges of the contract are governed by society in this world and Allah ﷻ in the Hereafter. Hence, marriage becomes a social and sacred institution promising an environment of continuity, protection and security within which a couple can develop themselves and the next generation of Muslims.

For some couples however, this process may be happening the other way around. It is the natural attraction for the opposite gender that has brought them together rather than the loftier ideals of serving Allah ﷻ through their commitment towards a new generation of Muslims. Regardless of whether it is the sexual or the nurturing instinct that leads to their coupling, both of these reasons are Islamically valid if they choose to pursue them through marriage. After all, the necessity of satisfying sexual urges is recognised in Islam. Most importantly, if the marital commitment and responsibilities are honestly observed, the initial sexual agenda will eventually lead to the fulfilment of its higher purpose, the perpetuation and development of the *ummah* (community of believers).

Admittedly, the marriage certificate cannot guarantee trust, fidelity and security, but it is not the written contract itself which is the purpose of marriage. Rather, it is the readiness to declare a commitment to each other, society and God. This subjects the declarants to enforceable rules of engagement which separates lip-service promises from genuine devotion. With this pact, marriage provides a safe psycho-emotional environment where the most intimate of pleasures can be explored.

By creating this exclusive zone for sexual indulgence, marriage simultaneously creates a social environment conducive to the cultivation of human souls. Yet, instead of being excluded, the status of sex and procreation is in turn elevated from a purely animalistic function to a revered position due to its role in accommodating new souls. In this way, marriage sanctifies sex and even elevates it to the status of worship, a concept which we will now explore further.

Sex as an Expression of Faith

Normally, we understand having faith in Allah ﷻ to mean obeying His command-ments as revealed through His Books, but it can also mean seeking harmony with the order of nature as that too is an expression of our faith in His wisdom. Thus, if sexual urges are part and parcel of our nature, enjoying sex is an expression of faith in God. Except that in the case of humans, our sense of right and wrong demands that we do it within a system that ensures accountability and responsibility for the emotional and psychological attachments arising from that union.

Within that framework, sexual enjoyment can be as good an expression of faith as any other form of worship can. In fact, it can be a deeply spiritual expe-rience if accompanied by the right attitude. This is comparable to the effect of sensory pleasures like food, scenery, fragrance and sound. For example, when we take the time to savour the myriad tastes of food, rather than gulping it down in haste, we actually experience God's creative genius on our taste buds. Similarly, when we are captivated by a mountain view or stopped in our tracks by the scent of jasmine in the air or lullabied by the trickling creek and they arouse in us a genuine sense of awe or gratefulness towards the Creator, they are as spiritual as spiritual goes.

The pleasure of sex can be more intense than any or even all other senso-ry enjoyments combined as it packs multiple human senses combined with the power of emotions and imagination, into one experience. Hence, we may glimpse a divine attribute in such an earthly act as the exquisite sensations of lovemaking are testimonies to the infinite ingenuity of Allah ﷻ in His act of Creation. That is why Imam Ghazali likened sexual pleasure to a sampling of Paradise, "The pleasure that is felt in sexual intercourse between a man and his wife is a little sign of the next worldly pleasure ... the greed for pleasure and happiness of Paradise lead a man towards guidance."[4]

It is no surprise then, that marriage is the norm in the life of the prophets ﷺ through the ages and the last Prophet ﷺ perpetuated that example and unequiv-ocally enjoined it upon us, his followers, "By Allah, I am more submissive to Allah and more afraid of Him than you; yet I fast and break my fast, I do sleep and I also marry women. So, he who does not follow my tradition in religion, is not from me (not one of my followers)" (Bukhari).

And We have already sent messengers before you and assigned to them wives
and descendants.
(Al-Ra'd 13:38)

The coming together of man and woman is a union initiated, enhanced and perpetuated by the synergy of opposites displaying the beauty of parity as a creative concept.

The above excerpts from the Quran and hadiths illustrate how enjoying sex expresses faith and evokes reverence for Allah ﷻ, but it is only valid and spiritually beneficial if the enjoyment complies with Allah's injunctions on appropriate behaviour. Above all, as with other examples of sensory pleasures, the believer must acknowledge that sex is not an end in itself but a means towards God-consciousness.

> God's Messenger ﷺ said, "In the sexual act of each of you there is a sadaqa." The Companions replied: "O Messenger of God! When one of us fulfils his sexual desire, will he be given a reward for that?" And he said, "Do you not think that were he to act upon it unlawfully, he would be sinning? Likewise, if he acts upon it lawfully he will be rewarded."
>
> (Muslim)

So, we see how marriage sanctifies sex and spiritualises its heavenly pleasures and how it makes it possible for carnal pleasures to conjure spiritual awareness of the Creator. Next, we look at how the ensuing experiences in marriage give rise to a kind of love which has the potential to reach the highest level in a person's relationship with God.

Marriage as a Crucible of Love

"Love" carries the most variable of meanings and definitions of itself, often riddled with confusion and misunderstanding, but let us now focus on the Quranic definition of love and marriage:

> Say, [O Muhammad], "If you should love Allah, then follow me, [so] Allah will love you and forgive you your sins. And Allah is Forgiving and Merciful."
>
> (Ali 'Imran 3:31)

This verse reveals a dimension of love which transcends emotions. Unlike the notion of love as an airy-fairy, euphoric, cloud-nine feeling as portrayed in pop culture, the Quran brings into love a practical dimension. It says that if believers are to love God, they should follow the one whom God loves just as when God loves, He forgives. Both following and forgiving require an active commitment that goes beyond emotion. Admittedly, feelings like affection, longing, tenderness and passion usually accompany an experience of love, but they are not love itself, as illustrated by the following thought experiment:

Imagine a neighbour who is so taken with your cat that she waxes lyrical about its colour, cuteness, softness and playfulness. You can visibly see how much she enjoys playing with it and she openly expresses how the cat delights and soothes her senses and how she misses it when it is not near. Believing, through observing her behaviour, that your neighbour loves your cat as you do, you ask her to care for it when you have a three-week overseas commitment. Much to your surprise, instead of jumping at the opportunity, she baulks at having to feed and bathe the animal, clean its litter bin and all the other responsibilities of caring for such an adorable creature. At this point, it is plain to see that your neighbour does not really love your cat. She may be infatuated, obsessed, mesmerised, but she is not in love.

The philosopher, Eric Fromm defines love as knowing, respecting, caring for and responding to[5] the beloved. We place their needs and well-being above our own and attend to them sincerely even when we are not asked to and even when it is not reciprocated. True love involves sacrifice, devotion and commitment, but it is not about spoiling, pampering or indulging the beloved's every desire. It is about empathising with their state of well-being – be it physical, mental, emotional or spiritual – and acting to improve or enhance it. As Fromm asserts, love is, "the active concern for the life and the growth of that which we love".[6]

It is significant that in Islamic teachings, messages of belief and servitude to God, rather than the love of God are predominant. The Prophet's sayings are not peppered with utterances of love for humanity or even for Allah ﷻ. He did exhort believers to love God and one another, "You will not enter Paradise until you believe and you will not believe until you love each other" (Muslim), but he did not talk endlessly about how deep his love for his *ummah* was. Instead, he loved them by enduring persecution, battling in wars, eschewing luxuries and dedicating his life to guiding and nurturing in order to spread the gift of Allah's message to all humankind. We are urged to love in the same manner, "Shall I show you something that, if you did, you would love each other? Spread peace between yourselves" (Muslim). Therefore, we should not mistake love for an intangible emotion that needs announcing repetitively lest the beloved does not know, but rather as the action of caring and attending to the beloved, whether they are aware of it or not and even if they are not thankful for it.

Likewise, loving God is more than filling our minds, hearts and tongues with His praises. Although feelings and expressions are part and parcel of the loving experience, still they are meaningless to Allah ﷻ unless followed up with the active concern that Eric Fromm talks of. Except that in the case of Allah ﷻ that concern is to be directed to His creations who are in need of it:

> *Righteousness is not that you turn your faces toward the east or the west, but [true] righteousness is [in] one who ... gives wealth, in spite of love for it, to relatives,*

orphans, the needy, the traveller, those who ask [for help], and for freeing slaves...
(Al-Baqarah 2:177)

Hence the maxim, "If ye do love Allah ﷻ, follow the Prophet ﷺ" is an all-encompassing approach towards loving God because, through the Prophet's teachings and examples we know, respect and respond to Allah ﷻ. Although submission and obedience are first planted in a believer's thought, speech and actions through the notions of Paradise and Hell, like carrots and sticks, it is only a beginning. Those who finally internalise the Prophet's teachings grow from acting on such conditional belief and obedience to God to pure unconditional servitude in mind, body and spirit, regardless of reward and punishment, but fully out of love and longing for the Creator; a state of love as described by the *Sufi* teacher, Rabi'atul Adawiyah:

> *Neither fear of Hellfire nor hope of a Heavenly reward excites my love*
> *and worship of God. If either were so, I would only be a bad employee*
> *working from fear of punishment and hope of benefit. My longing and*
> *love, rather, is the sole basis of my devotion to Him.*
>
> – Sufi Women[7]

So, contrary to common perceptions, in this understanding of love, it is not something that happens to you beyond your control, like a man chancing upon the perfect girl or Cupid striking someone's heart. It is something that YOU choose to happen because love is not what you receive, but what you give. In fact, it is only because it is within our choice to give love, that it is fair for the Prophet ﷺ to expect us to love one another. Not only would it be an unjust expectation, but it would also be futile to follow the Prophet ﷺ to attain love for God *(Ali 'Imran 3:31)*, if love were indeed beyond our control. This is in line with what we discussed in "Exclusive Zone of Sexual Indulgence"; that a human being is a unique creature who believes, obeys and ultimately loves God purely out of his choice and not His Design. That is the highest meaning of life for a Muslim. As proclaimed by Imam Ghazali in *Ihya Ulumuddin*, "Love of God is the last stage and the highest in rank, there is no higher stage after acquisition of love of God".[8]

Marriage and the ensuing family life are experiential cultivators of love. It is for this reason that love can blossom in arranged marriages even when couples hardly know each other initially. Love is something couples can choose. Those who choose to love will focus on the agreeable aspects of each other's looks, mannerisms, thoughts and character, while striving to reconcile the differences as they develop their love for each other. The passion, longing, tenderness and affection

SEX, SOUL AND ISLAM

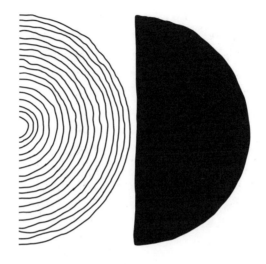

Marriage is a **mosaic** of beautiful and ugly experiences of spousal, parental, filial and sibling relationships. It brings together **joy** and **heartbreak**, trust and jealousy, loyalty and betrayal, and many other good and bad experiences in one **rich** but **intense** environment.

will follow suit once they establish their practical commitment to each other, aided by the natural attraction of sexual opposites.

Marriage is a mosaic of beautiful and ugly experiences of spousal, parental, filial and sibling relationships. It brings together joy and heartbreak, trust and jealousy, loyalty and betrayal, and many other good and bad experiences in one rich but intense environment, much akin to a crucible wherein the good and the bad may separate and be clarified or meld into something new and unpredictable.

With guidance, we learn to differentiate between the calculative favours we do for something in return and true unconditional loving. You can see it in the example of the couple who retains tender affection for each other into old age, even when all the youthful trappings of attraction have long since disappeared, or the siblings who stand up for one another against hostile strangers even as their own relationship is fraught with rivalry and jealousy, or the child who sacrifices the most gainful years of their career to look after estranged parents in their old age, or the parents who readily forgive their child's wrong-doings and ill treatment, even when that forgiveness is not sought.

There is a limit to which love can be explained and theorised. In the end, humankind has to experience what it is and what it is not – in real and practical terms. So, if indeed, "love of God is the last stage and the highest in rank" in our relationship with God, as according to Imam Ghazali, it is only fitting that marriage be the crucible that smelts and separates true from false love as marriage too is what brings us into this world. In the crucible of marriage we are prepared for the suffering and pleasure and all that it takes to unconditionally love God, humanity and the universe in mind, body and spirit. Not only that, but the kinship which marriage generates, binds us emotionally into cohesive units of society.

Sex, Marriage, Family, Kinship, Society

And of His signs is that He created for you from yourselves mates that you may
find tranquillity in them; and He placed between you love and mercy. Indeed, in
that are signs for a people who give thought.
(Al-Rum 30:21)

The conjuring of love from the sexual union of human beings is mentioned in this famous verse of the Quran and is widely taken as the defining purpose of marriage. In Chapter Four of this book, we will elaborate on how the natural force of attraction between opposite sexes in an enlightened sexual relationship, surpasses genital intercourse to involve a whole gamut of sensations, thoughts, emotions and imagination, such that the magic of sexual union multiplies whatever sense of closeness, exclusivity, loyalty, responsibility and care which exists between two mates. Of course, the positive atmosphere created by this not only benefits the couple. It sustains a lifetime of love and compassion, the perfect context within which to start a family.

> *And it is He who has created from water a human being and made him [a relative by] lineage and marriage. And ever is your Lord competent [concerning creation].*
> (Al-Furqan 25:54)

In his commentary of the Quran, Abdullah Yusuf Ali[9] explains the above verse:

> *(Through marriage) he (man) can trace lineage and pedigree, and thus remember and commemorate a long line of ancestors, to whom he is bound by ties of piety ... Further, there is the mystic union in marriage: it is not only like the physical union of animals but it gives rise to relationships arising out of the sexes of individuals who were not otherwise related to each other.*

The "mystic union of marriage" is a socially and spiritually binding vow which ratifies this natural sense of belonging and loyalty to blood-relations. The family then becomes the smallest of the network of institutions through which society is organised; its own well-being affecting that of the society at large and vice versa. So, if families are successful, it is as if half the quest is accomplished,

> *When a man marries, he indeed perfects half of his way of life. Then he should fear Allah ﷻ regarding the remaining half.*
> (Tabrani)

In that sense, the sexual phenomenon is vital to the development of societies, so much so that a sexless marriage is a cause for concern in Islam. Hence, sex and procreation were advocated by the Prophet ﷺ albeit with qualifications.

Previously, we discussed the adverse effects of boundless proliferation of off-spring on value development of the human young. However, bounded by the exclusive nurturing environment and system of responsibilities established through marriage, the Prophet ﷺ encouraged his followers to indulge the instinct to proliferate, "Marry prolific women and propagate your race, since I shall be proud of your numbers on the Day of Judgement" (Ahmad). As families grow exponentially, multiplying our numbers is one strategy of propagating and perpetuating God-consciousness as the prevalent culture among humanity. In proliferating the human race within the secure loving environment of marriage, we serve as God's agents in sustaining, nurturing and preparing His new vicegerents for their own roles in times to come.

It follows necessarily, that having big families must be accompanied by a high sense of responsibility to guide young souls well in this world in preparation for the Hereafter. Whilst the Prophet ﷺ hoped to be proud of our numbers, he also warned us of the futility of a large *ummah* which is not accompanied by the values and virtues which he extolled. The biggest danger to the ideal Islamic society is when a community loses sight of the next world and begins to love this world for its own sake.

> The Messenger said, *"The People will soon summon one another to attack you from every place in the same way that a pack calls around its prey."* Someone asked, *"Will that be because of our small numbers at that time?"* He replied, *"No, you will be numerous at that time: but you will be froth and scum like that carried down by a torrent (of water), and Allah ﷻ will take the fear of you from the breasts (hearts) of your enemy and cast al-wahn into your hearts."* Someone asked, *"O Messenger of Allah, what is al-wahn?"* He replied, *"Love of the world and dislike of death."*
>
> (Abu Dawud)

We see how marriage sanctifies sex for enabling mankind's physical existence in this world, celebrates its heavenly pleasures as a path to tranquillity, love and mercy between spouses and then utilises the kinship it generates to bind us emotionally into cohesive units of society. As such, marriage eventually must become part and parcel of the general framework of Islamic guidance – which includes laws applicable to all Muslims, married and unmarried. Next, we illustrate the interconnection between marriage and Islam as a whole, using examples of behavioural codes applicable outside of marriage which have proven indispensable in preserving the sanctity of sex.

Sex in the Scheme of Islam

> O mankind, fear your Lord, who created you from one soul and created from it its mate and dispersed from both of them many men and women. And fear Allah ... and the wombs.
>
> (Al-Nisa 4:1)

We revisit this Quranic verse to examine its impact on shaping a culture crucial to the development of human souls. After establishing that fact, the verse which starts by calling mankind to fear God, continues with an instruction to fear the wombs; in other words, to revere the womb. The original Quranic word used in the phrase "fear the wombs" and "fear your Lord" is shared by both which suggests the immense gravity of this warning to mankind. "Fear the wombs" is a grave warning to men against invading this sanctified space without authority and women against allowing it to be invaded – the womb being the site where souls are brought into this world through the process of mating and reproduction. Such warnings form the basis of Islam's zero tolerance of unlawful sexual intercourse:

> And do not approach unlawful sexual intercourse. Indeed, it is ever an immorality and is evil as a way.
>
> (Al-Isra 17:32)

A High Standard of Chastity

This intolerance is translated practically into the observation of chastity by all Muslims; men and women, married and unmarried, through a comprehensive set of precautions which, among others, are based on the following hadiths and Quranic verse:

> O Asma, when a woman reaches the age of menstruation, it does not suit her that she displays her parts of body except this and this, and he pointed to her face and hands.
>
> (Abu Dawud)

> Whoever believes in Allah and the Last Day must never be in privacy with women without there being a mahram (chaperone) with her, for otherwise Satan will be the third person (with them).
>
> (Ahmad)

> Tell the believing men to reduce [some] of their vision and guard their private parts. That is purer for them ... And tell the believing women to reduce [some] of their vision and guard their private parts and not expose their adornment except that which [necessarily] appears thereof and to wrap [a portion of] their headcovers over their chests ...
>
> (Al-Nur 24:30-31)

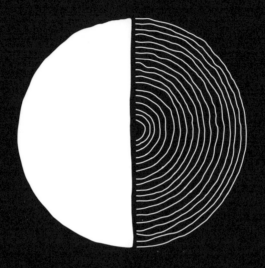

The pleasure of sex can be **more intense** than any or even all other sensory enjoyments combined as it packs **multiple human senses** combined with the power of **emotions** and **imagination**, into one experience.

These precautions are known collectively as the concept of *hijab* (veiling). For more details, you may refer to books like The Lawful and the Prohibited in Islam by Dr Yusuf al-Qardawi. Here, the concept of *hijab* is not limited to the headwear of Muslim women. In fact, it is not confined to women only but applies to both genders instead. The constituent aspects of the *hijab* concept are: a dressing code against flaunting of bodily beauty, rules prohibiting inter-mingling in private close proximity and the principle of "lowering the gaze" to avoid probing or lustful looks directed at bodily privacies, all of which apply to unrelated members of the opposite sex. However, the Prophet 🕌 also anticipated the possibilities of same-sex attractions, when he said,

> *A man shall not look at the aurat (nakedness) of another man, nor*
> *a woman of a woman, nor should a man go under one cloth with*
> *another man, nor a woman with another woman.*

(Muslim)

The concept of *hijab* works hand-in-hand with the institution of marriage in safe-guarding the sanctity of sex. *Hijab* defines acceptable behaviour for day-to-day cross-gender interactions, being essentially a system of pre-emptive precautions to nip fornication in its bud before it even has a chance to blossom. All these pre-cautions are in recognition of the strength of sexual attraction as real and powerful.

The alternative view might advocate free unrestricted interaction between the sexes as the best way to acquire control over sexual temptations as individuals learn to cope with the effects of dressing, bodily beauty, close proximity and priva-cy – hands on. The reality of sexual attraction though, will prove such advocacies over-optimistic. It is as wishful as pushing non-swimmers into the deep sea and expecting them to learn how to swim. Granted, some may learn, but more would drown. As a Muslim, whether or not you think you can control your sexual urges, the *hijab* concept discourages against over-confidence and inculcates a humbler attitude of caution in dealing with one of the strongest natural forces of attraction created by God.

Yet, it is not total separation from the opposite gender that *hijab* advocates. Equally harmful is the other extreme of complete segregation of the sexes as we see in some Muslim societies. The open secret of underground prostitution[10] and homosexuality[11] found in these societies was described by a Tunisian sociologist in his 1985 book, *Sexuality in Islam* and he attributed them directly to this excessive distortion of the *hijab* concept as well as the misogynistic abuses to be discussed in Chapter Two. The *hijab* concept is a moderate approach between these two extremes. The basic idea is to develop positive and respectful relationships between the sexes through cross-gender interactions in open, decent and non-scandalous settings, where the possibility of sexual exploitation and temptation is minimised.

While *hijab* plays its role of regulating cross-gender interaction, marriage complements it by providing an exclusive zone where sexual expression is indulged and cherished. Together, they become a behavioural standard through which the sexual instinct can remain in human control, "the womb" is treated with utmost regard and sex is sanctified in both theory and reality. Unfortunately, this complementarity is increasingly eroded by the laxity towards the *hijab* in the present day, sometimes even by married Muslim couples. We see this in so many cases of extra-marital affairs where the failure to observe *hijab* has opened a door to inappropriate intimacy. It is not down to any particular violation of the rulings, but rather the negligent attitude, even disdain, towards the whole concept of sexual boundaries which contributes towards many cases of so-called accidental affairs.

By modern Western standards, Islam's dressing and inter-mixing codes are seen as outdated and irrelevant and many Muslims under the influence of these "norms" have adopted a more casual standard of relationship with the opposite gender in the name of open-mindedness. Unfortunately, many of the cases of extra-marital relations we have handled in our counselling clinic have developed from such "harmless" encounters between colleagues or family friends. Typically, many of our clients had no prior intention of being unfaithful, seeking only to share their family problems or work difficulties with a sympathetic ear. However, sharing leads to the enjoyment of emotional comfort and the subsequent development of attachments and feelings that should really be reserved for one's spouse. Beyond this point, it takes little for emotional intimacy to become physical, even as they remember their status as family friends or working colleagues.

These seemingly "harmless" encounters have been encouraged by the advent of Facebook, Twitter, WhatsApp and other social media platforms. Admittedly, social media has been a great boon to communication and life in general, but it is not without its problems. We are seeing increasing cases of extra-marital affairs originating from supposedly harmless flirting in cyber-space between friends, colleagues and old flames (many of whom are married themselves). The physical distance provided by social media platforms allows a flirtatious compliment to reach an old flame, friend or colleague directly. As a norm, if it is not appreciated, the recipient will simply ignore the comment and no harm is done as the rejection is easier on both the rejected and the rejector when expressed on the internet rather than face-to-face. Unfortunately, this has also led to it becoming an excellent cover for flirting and "testing of the water" for those yearning for excitement amidst the daily grind of mid-marriage. Problems start when a kind response triggers the kind of chain-reaction we described in the last paragraph.

That is precisely why Islam pre-empts the power of cross-gender attraction which can creep up on us surreptitiously. Social barriers we maintain with strangers can be eroded with familiarity through the exchange of ideas, opinions and views which leads to the opening of hearts through the sharing of feelings and emotions, culminating in inappropriate intimacy – even if it all started as platonic in nature. This can, in turn, ignite the search for physical closeness as the natural next step in the relationship between the male and female. Intellectual and emotional intimacy between colleagues may start off innocently sexless, but if left untampered, it tends to seek out the missing dimensions like the sensual and sexual to complete the intimate experience.

This is not to suggest that it will always happen this way. Rather, when an accidental affair happens, this is how innocently it can begin. The non-physical encounters can grow into full-blown sexual infidelity, even if unintended by both parties. Even in cases where an affair remains online and the two never meet, the betrayal is still as hurtful to the cheated party and no less damaging for the marriage. It may not happen to everybody who engages in such encounters, but it is like playing with fire as the risk that it will grow into something beyond our control is ever present.

These are not theories but our broad stroke observations across the cases of extra-marital affairs we have come across – many of which are classified by the perpetrators as unintentional. Hence, we urge married couples not to be too casual about those private meetings with friends, colleagues or in some circumstances even relatives, of the opposite gender, regardless of the reason. Unfortunately, being relatives is no guarantee of protection and we say this in view of our cases of accidental affairs involving nieces and uncles, nephews and aunties and between in-laws.

Such meetings are not completely forbidden, but Islam asks for the exercising of caution through avoiding private gatherings between two people, maintaining modesty and avoiding inappropriate "banter". It is not about the fanatic implementation of such rules and in certain situations, the believer must use their discretion, but if you realise that you are looking forward to such encounters or they are becoming too intimate or too frequent, do not feel bad about taking these *hijab* precautions – instead of being pressured to fit in by proving you are open-minded or modern.

Hijab is an example of Islam's teachings which does not directly address the institution of marriage but crucially supports it by sanctifying sex. The Islamic belief of sex as something sacred does not remain an airy-fairy notion but is actualised in the daily life of its believers and this process requires collective participation of the community as guided by the *hijab* code of interaction between genders. Interestingly, although *hijab* is part of Islamic law and in consequence, what is permitted and what is forbidden is clearly defined, it does not come with stipulated punishments. There are reports of admonitions like the hadith involving Asma that was presented at the beginning of this section, but there are no records of punishments meted out by the Prophet or advised by the Quran for violation of *hijab* rulings[12]. It is plausible these were never needed in the time of the Prophet due to voluntary compliance by the his contemporaries, but it could also be due to the efficacy of Islamic law when it is implemented holistically. In totality, there is a spectrum of severity among the laws and at one extreme is the infamous punishment of stoning to death for adultery which we will explore further, later in this chapter. Suffice to say that the full range of Islamic guidance works to induce a social environment where sexual purity is highly prized while illicit sex is detested.

Zero Tolerance of Non-marital Sex

The Quranic word for non-marital sex is *zina* and it refers to sexual intercourse out of wedlock,[13] be it fornication if the person is not married or adultery if they are. Islam's abhorrence of it stems from verse *Al-Nisa 4:1* in the Quran which commands humankind not to violate the sanctity of the "womb". Non-marital sex is regarded as one of the greatest sins in Islam. But why?

In *Cultural and Social Anthropology*, the writers state that "taking human societies as a whole, the majority accept premarital sexual experimentation without serious disapproval". They note that, "chastity is an unknown virtue among natives. At an early age they become initiated into sexual life" and that "premarital activity may function among primitives to prepare young people for marriage".[14] In An Introduction to Anthropology, the writers look at the historic norms of pre-marital sex in pre-modern cultures around the globe from the Masai in Africa to the Samoans in the Pacific.[15] Yet this inclination is not confined to these older communities as a 2014 global survey by Pew Research Center across 40 nations recorded that those who regard premarital sex as unacceptable are still in the minority.[16] These findings suggest that, left to our own devices, humanity would rather conduct its sexual affairs without the prohibitions prescribed through exclusive sex zones. So why shouldn't we?

If *zina* is the natural human tendency, that implies that chastity or sexual purity is more of an alien introduction to our nature. As disturbing as it may seem, this could actually be our reality, but only in part. The predisposition to *zina* is the trait we share with the animal kingdom, whereas the complete human reality comprises of mind, body and soul. When the mind and soul come into play, human attitudes

SEX, SOUL AND ISLAM

towards sex begin to change and vary and when illicit sex is abhorred and sexual purity preferred, it is not an inborn, instinctive inclination but a learned trait. From the Islamic perspective, this trait is not a human construct. It was introduced from beyond human origins, involving the work of prophets and passed on through a life-long, inter-generational process of inculcation. Divinely ordained, this trait distinguishes the human being from other animals.

This is the fundamental reason for the resolute anti-*zina* culture in Islam. That is why its implementation is comprehensive, involving all three aspects of Islamic teachings, namely faith, law and morality, as discussed at the start of this chapter. Now, we will explore the interplay of faith, law and morality in relation to how a common belief in sexual exclusivity is entrenched conceptually, legally and formatively in Islam. First, we look at the conceptual necessity for a culture of sexual purity, specifically in terms of the sex-soul interaction. Then we look at the role of law in cultivating sexual ideals. We then go on to investigate whether the core ideal behind Islamic sex-related laws *(Al-Rum 30:21)* has been realised in Muslim societies in Chapter Two. Finally, if the anti-*zina* values of Islam distinguish humans from animals in concept and action, Chapter Four discusses how this distinction is instilled into the character and relationship of the married believers as it expounds a formative hadith which distinguishes mating from lovemaking.

A Culture of Sexual Purity

The soul, or *ruh* in Arabic, experiences sexuality only because of its placement in an animal body for life on Earth. As we are told in the Noble Quran, it was blown into the human body at the completion of its creation *(Al-Hijr 15:29)*. Upon coming to life, the new creation showed a capacity for comprehension surpassing that of the angels *(Al-Baqarah 2:30-33)*. Then, each of these completed creations was called upon to acknowledge the Creator before their sojourn on Earth *(Al-A'raf 7:172)*. Significantly, the human element that was involved in this testimony was not the soul per se. Instead, the verse mentions *anfus*, the plural for *nafs*, which is best translated as "self". This distinction between the human soul and human self is key in understanding the sex-soul interaction and the necessity of sexual restraint.

The soul is only one element in the mind-body-soul composition of the human self. The body is another. Interestingly, sex is only a subset of this bodily element, but it can wreak havoc to the soul if left to its own devices, no less because the material body was created out of earth *(Al-Hijr 15:28)*, for material Life on Earth. Hence, from the onset of our creation, sex, although only a sub-element of the total human self, has the home-ground advantage over the spiritual soul, as well as team support from other bodily instincts of self-preservation and species-perpetuation.

Still, together they all travel as components of the human being, undergoing Earthly trials in preparation for the Hereafter.

The Quran alludes to a tussle between the body and the soul within the human self as explained by Muhammad Fazl-ur-Rahman Ansari.[17] It tells of the "carnal self" and its propensity towards the pleasures of the flesh *(Yusuf 12:53)*. This is when animal instincts are predominant in the disposition of a human being, the sexual kind included. However, when the soul prevails, conscience predominates in the human self to reproach and steer the human being towards what is right. After all, the soul did come directly from Allah ﷻ, blown into the perfected body *(Al-Hijr 15:29)*. In this state it is called the "reproaching self" *(Al-Qiyamah 75:2)*. The "carnal" and "reproaching" selves are not two entities but rather two polarities of the same human entity being pulled in different directions by two of its three constituent elements. The successful human being is the one who balances the two polarities well to lead a productive life in this world for a good placement in the Hereafter. This is a state called the "self-at-peace" *(nafs ulmutmainnah),* the self that will eventually be invited into Paradise *(Al-Fajr 89:27-30)*.

Although the body has home ground advantage and support from "team world", the soul is fortified by the third element of the self, the intellect or the capacity to comprehend the meaning of things *(Al-Baqarah 2:30-33)* and as they say, knowledge is power. Not only that, but the "mind-body-soul" is only a simplified model of our *nafs*. There are other means of comprehension referred to variously as the heart, feelings, sense, intuition, imagination and inspiration. These are essentially intersections between the three basic elements in operation. Suffice to say, they enrich the human experience, complement intellectual comprehension and provide the soul with potential advantage, not only in defeating, but even in recruiting the body in its quest towards Paradise.

However, it is only a potential advantage. The immediate tangible allure of this world can too often surmount it. As anthropological studies teach us, throughout the history of humanity, the "carnal self" has prevailed. For the "reproaching self" to have real advantage over the "carnal", Divine intervention becomes inevitable. The solution provided by Allah ﷻ is the comprehensive approach of inculcating an abhorrence towards free sex while creating exclusive, secure and wholesome zones for sexual enjoyment among Muslims. This is the "why". As for the "how", that is where the law and its implementation comes into play.

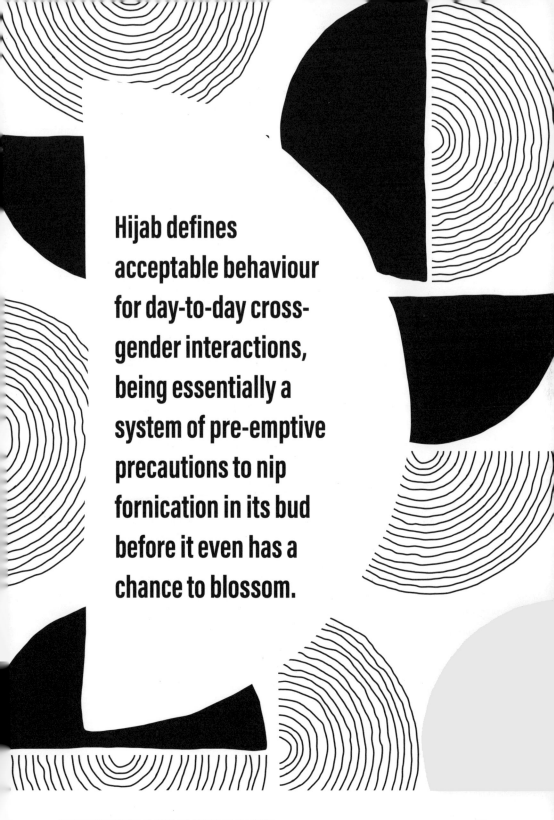

Hijab defines acceptable behaviour for day-to-day cross-gender interactions, being essentially a system of pre-emptive precautions to nip fornication in its bud before it even has a chance to blossom.

The Role of Law in Cultivating Ideals

In putting concepts into practice, Divine injunctions are like implementable ground rules and a road map from which believers figure out what, when and how to fulfil their responsibilities. The vast corpus of Islamic jurisprudence is given over to guidance on how to do things; ranging from personal hygiene, to worship, right through to social welfare, rather than to punishments. With regards to sex, the set of *hijab* rulings should guide society towards a foundational environment of responsible cross-gender interaction upon which the culture of sexual purity emerges naturally. Unfortunately, there is no guarantee that all Muslims will adhere, but as long as infringements can be addressed through admonition (or minor punishments), corporal punishments are not needed. It is only when the defiance of such rulings become so brazen as to challenge the very foundation of the culture itself that such punishments become necessary.

These are the limits [set by] Allah, and whoever obeys Allah and His Messenger will be admitted by Him to gardens [in Paradise] under which rivers flow, abiding eternally therein; and that is the great attainment. And whoever disobeys Allah and His Messenger and transgresses His limits - He will put him into the Fire to abide eternally therein, and he will have a humiliating punishment.

(Al-Nisa 4:13-14)

The Arabic word *hudud* is plural for *had* or limit, alluding to Allah's boundaries which should not be crossed *(Al-Nisa 4:13-14)*. The idea behind *hudud* is a punishment so harsh that its mere existence deters the general public from approaching certain extremely egregious crimes.

Hudud can also refer to the upper limit of punishments. Either way, both meanings point to *hudud* being intended as the very last resort in punishing the most grievous of crimes; but only after generous mitigating considerations have been applied and stringent prosecution prerequisites have been complied with. In the case of *zina* accusations, the prerequisite is four honourable Muslim men who visually saw the penile penetration of the vagina during the crime. Anything less will be dismissed and it has been argued that such a scenario is completely implausible, making the prerequisite impossible to fulfil and rendering the punishment redundant and thus never intended by Allah ﷻ for implementation. However, we would beg to differ. A situation in which four people or more can witness *zina* happening may be uncommon, but it is not unheard of. An orgy, for example, involves far more than four people, not counting the cheering watchers and evidence of such acts can be easily obtained via the internet. On account of personal freedom, some people actually take pride in outdoing the primal behaviour of animals during sex. In view of the command "fear the womb", a Muslim's involvement in such a blatant defiance of Allah ﷻ and His Word must demand nothing less than a severe consequence.

As for the punishment, stipulated in the Quran is a hundred lashings (Al-Nur 24:2), but classical jurisprudence stipulated one hundred lashings for fornication and stoning for adultery based on reasons which are out of our scope. In any case, it is still very harsh, by modern standards not least. The idea is that the combined effect of *hudud* deterrent, social compliance with the *hijab* code and advocacy of marital sex work together to create a chaste society; very much like that which prevailed during the Prophet's lifetime where the crime of *zina* and consequently, its punishment, were virtually non-existent. Typically, its detractors characterise it as draconian, backward and a violation of individual human rights, but such labels are subjective. For example, the expression of total freedom through free sex is seen as the ultimate symbol of human progress by some, while others see that as regression into primitive behavioural standards. Either way, what is most important is that we do not violate the rights of others in the process of upholding our beliefs.

For Muslims, the corporal punishment is a deterrent reminder and a symbolic marker of the sanctity of sex. It is within our human rights to protect this sanctity the way we deem fit within our community in territories we have authority to govern. Implementing this law does not violate the individual rights of those who do not believe in it. This is clear when we understand the law completely, from stipulation to prosecution. The stringent prosecution prerequisite of four upright witnesses ensures that we do not over-zealously punish fornicators when they have enough decency to exercise their supposed basic human right to fornicate behind closed doors. In such cases, this violation becomes a matter between them and Allah ﷻ.

The high burden of proof attests to the fact that the *hudud* targets the blatantly recalcitrant fornicators with an agenda to undermine our values of decency through such open displays of defiance that their debauchery is witnessable by four morally upright members of our society. If such cases occur, it is the Muslim community's right to public decency that is being trampled upon and we have the right to address it. The threat of a severe punishment is one option for deterring or removing such a blatant assault on our collective right to decency within territories we have authority to govern, should alternative measures fail.

However, this is not a call for the return of stoning in our times; nor its opposition. Here, we are merely explaining Muslims' basic human rights to initiate and protect our cherished value of chastity among ourselves. How far the *sharia* should go in protecting the Islamic values of chastity within our communities is best de-

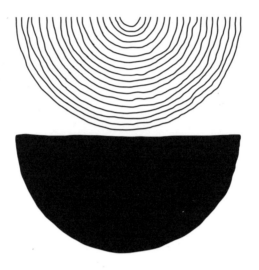

If *zina* is the **natural** human **tendency**, that implies that **chastity** or sexual purity is more of an **alien** introduction to our nature. As disturbing as it may seem, this could actually be our **reality**, but only **in part**.

cided by experts in jurisprudence and socio-political fields. As marital counsellors, our interest is in the inculcation of this value on the personal level and by extension, in the wider Muslim culture.

We have discussed why a culture of sexual purity and exclusivity is crucial for the soul's safe passage through life on Earth. By this juncture we have explained that this conceptual ideal of sexual purity does not remain theoretical but is practically implemented through a wide spectrum of Divine injunctions which initiate and also protect it. In other words, what we accept as a matter of faith is actualised through the agency of law. Equally important, though, is that law in Islam is not for its own sake. There is always an ideal which law seeks to establish.

Conclusion

Although the element of sex is not central to the Islamic faith, it still occupies a crucial role in the meaning of life from an Islamic perspective. For the believers, sex is not regarded as a necessary evil or a hindrance to spiritual growth. Instead, it is positively capitalised on to create a conducive environment for couples and the wider community to develop comprehensively. Marriage **sanctifies** sex for enabling human beings' physical existence in this world, **celebrates** its heavenly pleasures as a conjuror of tranquillity, love and mercy between spouses and **utilises** the kinship it generates to bind us emotionally into cohesive units of society – making marriage one of the most potent resource for humankind to fulfil its role as vicegerent on Earth. In the next chapter we discuss how well these ideals of marriage have been realised in Muslim societies.

Only a naïve or dishonest mind could be
surprised at the gaps that exist in any society
between its ideals and its practices.

ABDELWAHAB BOUHDIBA

Chapter 2

What's the Deal with Conjugal Rights?

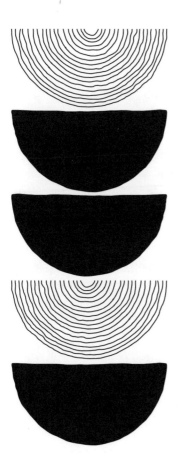

And of His signs is that He created for you from yourselves mates that you may find
tranquillity in them; and He placed between you love and mercy. Indeed in that are
signs for a people who give thought.
(Al-Rum 30:21)

At the end of Chapter One, we established that law in Islam is not for its own
sake. There is always a conceptual value behind any ruling, which in this case, as
revealed in the verse above, is spousal love and mercy invoked via the tranquillity
of sexual intimacy. Chapter Two looks at how far Muslim societies embrace this
value in their observance of Divine injunctions and Prophetic sayings regarding
conjugal rights.

Brief Overview of Islamic Law

Then We put you, [O Muhammad], on an ordained way concerning the matter
[of religion]; so follow it and do not follow the inclinations of those who do not
know ... This [Quran] is enlightenment for mankind and guidance and mercy for
a people who are certain [in faith].
(Al-Jathiyah 45:18 ... 20)

The word "way" in the verse above is a translation from the word *sharia* used in the
Arabic text. Literally, it means "path to a watering hole". Metaphorically, it signifies
the path leading to our Islamic goal and refers to the aspect of Islamic teachings
which provides practical, implementable guidance to fulfil our duties and responsibilities. Thus, it can be fairly referred to as "Divine law" or "Divine injunctions".

The principal source of this guidance is the Quran, followed by the Sunna, a
collection of examples set by the Prophet 🕮 and narrated via hadiths and lastly,
human judgment, in that order of priority. This hierarchy of guidance applies to
every aspect of Islamic life and takes from the instruction the Prophet 🕮 gave to
his representatives:

On the eve of his journey to Yemen, the Prophet asked Muadh
ibn Jabbal "How will you decide (or, judge) things when you be
called upon to do so?" He replied, "According to the Book of Allah,"
(Again the Prophet enquired) "When you do not find something (i.e.
clear instruction) in the Book of Allah, then how do you decide?"
(Thereupon) he replied, "I shall follow the method of the Messenger."
(The Prophet again asked) "If you do not find something in the

example of the Prophet, (then how)?" Then he replied, "I shall exercise my judgement"...

(Tirmidhi)

Using the same principle, the *sharia* was classified into teachable subjects like *ibada* (prescribed devotion), *mu'amala* (financial transaction), *faraidh* (inheritance), *aqdiya* (judiciary), *siyasa* (politics), as well as *munakahat* (marriage and family law), among others – to provide practical guidance to the Muslim masses. The one most relevant to marriage and sexual practices is *munakahat.* Therein are laws, rulings and etiquettes of sexual interaction meant to provide practical guidance so spous-es know what to expect and what to do for a mutually blissful sexual experience.

We will not be enumerating these subjects here as they are available in more authoritative books, for example the classic *Fiqhus Sunna* by Sayid Sabiq. Instead, we share our reflections on how such a comprehensive framework of guide-lines can be so misapplied in contemporary society as to result in a prevalently male-serving sexual dynamic within marriages as we observe through our own counselling experience. In the interests of fairness and accuracy, we begin with a cursory study of sexual history and contemporary global headline stories to fathom how real and prevalent this situation really is.

We will also look at how the wrongful or misguided implementation of the *sharia* impacts individual marriages and offer our analysis of what is causing the mismatch between sexual ideals and the reality as we see it, as well as suggesting solutions on how to correct the mismatch through a fair treatment of the sexual laws in their totality. Through this thorough analysis, we hope to reframe the common under-standing of conjugal rights to serve both genders better.

Ideals and Reality of Islamic Sexual Values

An enduring Western caricature of the sexual dynamics between men and women in Islam is the *harem* of the Muslim kings who were "surrounded by hundreds of semi-naked women, in an atmosphere of heavy perfume, cool fountains, soft mu-sic, and over-indulgence in every conceivable kind of vice".[18] This image portrays Muslim women as mere servants to men – segregated, kept as "virtual prisoners",[19] and "their principal duties ... to stay out of sight and to bear children".[20] On the other side of the same coin is the portrayal of the "orthodox Muslim lady", the idealised heroine of the school of "pure love" which purportedly inspired the European chivalric ideal of a "Lady". Here, the Muslim woman is characterised as a product of "a masculine game designed to satisfy intellectualised masculine emotions."[21] In other words, the "orthodox Muslim lady" was defined by men's narratives of noble femininity. So, when Muslim society is viewed through popular depictions of history, the Western eye sees it as "the last bastion of female subservience."[22]

Naturally, knowing the Quranic ideal of sex as a source of tranquillity, love and mercy between the sexes, we as Muslims resent the depiction above as a typical Western misconception. Yet, we should not neglect to critique the way in which our own communities have perpetuated these harmful interpretations of the *sharia*. Tunisian Muslim Professor of Sociology, Abdelwahab Bouhdiba asserts in his book *Sexuality in Islam* that the sexual reciprocity revealed in the Quran is lost in practice and "the Quranic balance, has, in actual fact, rarely been attained!"[23] As a result, "women (have been) reduced to the role of housewife and mother, providing children, and supervising the running of their husband's household,"[24] throughout Islamic history. He adds, "only a naïve or dishonest mind could be surprised at the gaps that exist in any society between its ideals and its practices."[25]

Bouhdiba goes on to illustrate that, despite the Quranic notion of the "complementarity of the sexes," where, "woman is not a mere possession of man … and man in turn is not the woman's possession,"[26] male bad faith … betrays women, sexuality and pleasure in a thousand and one ways,"[27] through the abuse of concubinage, gender segregation and inheritance laws, aggravated by a history of underground homosexual practices, prostitution and the production of obscene erotica in many Muslim societies. As a result, women have been reduced, "to the rank of playthings whose sole purpose (is) the satisfaction of the sexual selfishness of more or less blasé males".[28] He concludes, "Arabo-Muslim society is still largely male-worshipping, in essence and in its appearances, in its deep structures and in its superficial manifestations".[29]

Many of us would like to deny that this represents us today. Some will argue that the Professor is an Arab, "situating sexuality in the Arab-Muslim societies", whereas not all Muslims are Arabs nor do we adopt their excesses of past and present. Some may contend that a 250-page sociological study condensing thirteen centuries of sexual shenanigans is bound to produce an inordinate picture of excesses, not to mention inadvertently missing the less salacious and thus unrecorded examples of the harmony that exists in the majority of Muslim marriages throughout history. After all, the professor does mention that, "the system of concubinage, as indeed that of polygamy in general, affected only the towns, and even then the better-off classes … the rural world was characterised by greater stability of the family."[30]

Still, we cannot deny that the ingrained culture of misogyny is part and parcel of our history no more than we can deny that sexual subjugation of women still persists in modern Muslim societies in the form of forced marriages, the sexualisation of underage girls, domestic abuse and a vast array of other forms of oppression.

We cannot deny that **sexual subjugation** of women still persists in **modern** Muslim societies in the form of **forced** marriages, the sexualisation of **underage** girls, domestic **abuse** and a vast array of other forms of **oppression**.

They can be found in rural and urban settings and in diasporic communities re-
siding in the West. Even *if* they are not the norm, their mere existence betrays our
failure to embrace the spirit of sexual reciprocity of *Ar-Rum 30:21*. One of the prime
examples of the modern manifestation of female subservience is 'The Obedient
Wives Club.' Formed in 2011 in Malaysia with branches in Asia, Australia and the UK,
the club promotes polygamy and sexual subservience of wives to guarantee the
fidelity of their husbands. They are most well-known for that notorious soundbite:
wives must "serve their husbands better than a first-class prostitute". [31]

It is a great source of disappointment to us that such organisations exist and
shows that our society today has not progressed sufficiently from the male-serving
sexual viewpoint. Our own experience of counselling couples has exposed us to the
reality that many Muslims still regard sexual intercourse as chiefly a wife's religious
duty and a man's religious right. Many women are still clueless regarding sexual
pleasure and their rights to it and even among those who know of their sexual
rights, many do not bother to pursue them as they do not miss something they
never possessed in the first place. No doubt, bad sex is normally a contributing
factor, rather than the root cause of marital dysfunctions, but when it is a problem,
the sex invariably reflects a male-dominant dynamic that exists in other aspects
of marital life. Unfortunately, these male-serving sexual attitudes are exhibited by
both men and women at various stages of marriage.

We have listened to several cases of husbands throwing a tantrum on honeymoon nights because their new brides were unavailable for consummation due
to menstruation – as if it was within their control. We have met many wives who
have spent their entire marriage providing one-way sexual satisfaction until age
takes its toll on their bodies and makes them less satisfying to their self-serving
husbands. Then, having provided and raised children, these women feel they have
fulfilled their wifely duty and thus find their marriages with their sexually insatiable
and emotionally abusive husbands simply meaningless – especially in the case of
socio-economically independent women. Sadder still, are those dependent on their
husbands in old age. Whereas in younger days, they were more able to endure the
discomforts of sex which focuses solely on male gratification, in menopausal old
age they are forced to endure its pain. And what could be more degrading to a wife
than the husband who insists on indulging in good-bye sex on the night of his offi-
cial declaration of divorce, with the wife relenting out of a religious sense of duty?

Even if you can possibly argue that these husbands actually have their rights
covered by sexual laws in Islam, the question is, where is the love, mercy and tranquillity of *Al-Rum 30:21* in such cases? In fact, mutuality, reciprocity and equitability
seem to be largely missing from sociological observations of Muslim sexual mores,

SEX, SOUL AND ISLAM

both past and present. It seems quite difficult to deny that the conjugal rights of men are far better protected than that of women in Muslim societies.

Of course, this is not just an "Islamic problem". A broader study of sexual history reveals this one-sided sexual dynamic in other societies too. Reay Tannahill's *Sex in History* shows the subjugation of women as a common thread of human history, from the prehistoric world to the civilisations of the Near East, Egypt, Europe, Asia and the Americas. In *Sexuality – Insights and Issues*, Jerrold Greenberg asserts:

> *Historically, the role of the woman as a sexual partner has been to satisfy male needs. In India, for example, women were viewed as nothing without men. In the West, women who enjoyed sexual activity dared not speak of it publicly because of the severe penalties for doing so. Throughout the ages, women were viewed as the property of men ... in many societies men enjoyed a vastly superior status to women ... The ancient Greeks believed ... men had a higher nature and deserved greater privileges ... Throughout medieval times, women were thought to be inferior to men ... Some believe Aristotle's claim that the female was little more than an incomplete male ... However, the mid to late 1800s and the early 1900s witnessed many advancements in the status of women ... But whether we have achieved enough equality between the sexes is still a matter of debate.[32]*

Observed from a broader perspective, female subjugation is admittedly more of a universal human flaw than a peculiar Islamic trait. We highlighted examples involving Muslims only to pre-empt the predictable denials that it is a problem among our own communities. Whether these sociological evidences of female subjugation are statistically representative of us or whether we are in fact the last bastion of female subservience from the Western viewpoint, is missing the point. Sexual subjugation of women is absolutely unacceptable in Islam and has no place in a Muslim marriage. Rather than defending and denying, it is far more productive to try and comprehend how this male-serving understanding of conjugal rights arises. With this awareness, couples are better placed to deal with it together and work towards the sexual bliss of *Al-Rum 30:21* and the mutuality of that bliss as mentioned in *Al-Baqarah*:

> *... They are a clothing for you and you are a clothing for them ...*
> (Al-Baqarah 2:187)

Origins of Sexual Machismo Among Muslims

When a man invites his wife to his bed and she does not come, and he
(the husband) spends the night being angry with her, the angels curse
her until morning.

(Muslim)

This is probably the most quoted hadith in discussions about sex in Islam. In counselling sessions, we have heard both the pious and less observant husbands alike
relate this hadith with aplomb in order to defend their perceived conjugal rights.
Through the misuse of this hadith, many a wife's discomfort, dissatisfaction, fatigue
and preoccupation with housework and child-rearing are summarily dismissed
as mere excuses. Unfortunately, there are a large number of women who do not
dare challenge the common interpretation of this hadith and relent to the most
unreasonable and untimely sexual advances of their husbands at the expense of
their feelings and well-being. The more well-read husbands will also throw in the
following hadiths for good measure:

If a man calls his wife, then let her come, even if she is busy at the oven.

(Tirmidhi)

If a man calls his wife to his bed, let her respond, even if she is riding
her camel [i.e. very busy].

(al-Bazzar)

What further compounds the problem is when violence is involved. Men who believe that these prophetic sayings guarantee their absolute conjugal right, can easily
believe that they have the right to access them by any means. Hence, so many
husbands have been known to use physical and emotional coercion on their wives
to extract sexual gratification. In their minds, forceful sex against an unwilling wife is
legitimised by the conjugal right accorded to them by marriage. This juxtaposition
of the criminal use of force to assert a legally guaranteed right has made marital
rape deeply contentious, even among Muslim clerics and scholars.[33]

Ironically, Muslim male chauvinists are united with Islamophobes in using certain hadiths to insist that Islam sanctions male chauvinism to the point of sexual
coercion. However, this is not in keeping with the example of the Prophet ﷺ who
was known for his gentleness and kindness towards his wives. In a hadith reported by Tirmidhi, the Messenger of Allah ﷺ tells us, "The most complete of the

believers in faith, is the one with the best character. And the best of you are those who are best to their women". Another hadith recorded by Imam Muslim narrates that on one occasion the Prophet ﷺ refused a neighbour's exclusive invitation to a meal twice, until the neighbour, in his third attempt, included the Prophet's wife who was walking alongside him, in their invitation. Thus, would he take care not to hurt his wives, physically or emotionally.[34] In fact, his wife Aisha ؓ said of him:

> The Prophet ﷺ has not ever beaten any woman, any servant or anything in his hand other than fighting in the way of Allah the Almighty. He does not take revenge on anyone who harmed him except when breaching the orders of Allah the Almighty, in which case, he takes revenge.
>
> (Nasai)

The Prophet's manner towards his wives is at odds with the misogynistic and abusive interpretations of the first three hadith statements. Were his words inconsistent with his character or was he simply erratic in behaviour and speech? Or is this the case of the three blind men individually mistaking an elephant for a snake, a tree and a rope respectively as they grope its trunk, leg and tail separately? This old *sufi* tale tells us how a subject can be grossly misinterpreted if not considered in its totality. Likewise, a comprehensive study of sex-related hadiths reveals that the Prophet ﷺ directed three different kinds of sexual advice at wives, husbands and the couple as a collective entity. All three categories must be read as a whole or else it can lead to gross distortions of the message.

Sex Hadiths For Wives

> When a man invites his wife to his bed and she does not come, and he (the husband) spends the night being angry with her, the angels curse her until morning.
>
> (Muslim)

> If a man calls his wife, then let her come, even if she is busy at the oven.
>
> (Tirmidhi)

> If a man calls his wife to his bed, let her respond, even if she is riding her camel [i.e. very busy].
>
> (al-Bazzar)

The first category of sexual hadiths is directed towards women and addresses an important sexual characteristic of men which women do not experience. A man's sexual arousal is triggered through a wider range of stimulatory means and thus is likely to occur more often and more easily than a woman's (we discuss this further in Chapter Four). As most women experience their sexual desires in a different way to men, a wife may unwittingly dismiss her husband's frequent advances as over-indulgent and expect him to control and curb his lust until a more suitable time – very much like what she herself is capable of. There is every possibility that the Prophet 🕌, who assisted members of his *ummah* with their most intimate and pressing problems, was privy to such cases in his own lifetime.[35] Hence, the above hadiths were timely and relevant reminders to wives to be sensitive to their husbands' feelings and wary of making them feel rejected by dismissing their advances.

Even today, in the counselling sessions we hold, husbands will confide, often for the first time, the deep hurt which they feel as a result of their wives' mocking or sneering at the frequency of their romantic overtures. During one session, a husband expressed how his wife's indifference to his sexual advances would make him feel like a dog whimpering for scraps of food. Sometimes, those curt retorts genuinely stem from ignorance of men's sensitivities, but sometimes they are de-liberate payback for general mistreatment on the part of husbands. As many wives are the major homemakers and caregivers of the family, their hectic routine can take its toll on romance and lovemaking after years of marriage.

The appropriate reaction in such scenarios is not simply to give in to a hus-band's advances. The healthier route involves addressing the day-to-day grievanc-es which are often at the root of sexual unwillingness or supposed indifference. Sometimes, this requires an intense period of counselling, but often, it is just a matter of minimal coaching on communication skills like how to diplomatically refuse a request for sex, be it with humour, intonation, displays of affection, sincere promises or sweet talk. Sometimes it involves coaching husbands on how to take such "rejections" in their stride. Although the central issue may be the unwillingness of the wife, the solution requires effort from both parties.

It is important to note that this group of hadiths speaks to women about the damage on their own souls caused by making their husbands feel rejected. They are meant for wives to reflect upon. They say nothing about husbands being given vigilante rights to exercise their own punishments and they become counter-pro-ductive when men abuse them to ensure their own sexual satisfaction.

Many women are still clueless regarding sexual pleasure and their rights to it and even among those who know of their sexual rights, many do not bother to pursue them as they do not miss something they never possessed in the first place.

Sex Hadiths For Husbands

When any of you has sex with his wife, be earnest. When your desire is fulfilled before hers, do not stop until her desire is fulfilled.

(Abu Ya'la)

In three matters, the weakness of a male is expressed ... (thirdly) the man who approaches his wife and thereby fulfils his (sexual) desire from her before she fulfilled hers from him.

(Dailami)

If many women cannot appreciate why men are so easily and frequently turned on, even more men are completely clueless as to why women are not. They expect their wives to be as easily aroused as they are and by the same kind of stimulation that arouses them. In fact, many couples fail to understand the fundamental difference between male and female sexual stimulation. After a while, most don't bother anymore as they find a way to survive a lifetime of monotonous one-sided sex. The wives may suffer quietly, resent passively or tolerate willingly. They may simply disengage during sex. The husbands rarely complain as their sexual needs are served either way. Inevitably, a purely male-serving sexual relationship falls short of the ideals of *Al-Rum 30:21* and *Al-Baqarah 2:187* and places immense strain on the wider marital relationship.

The Prophet ﷺ pre-empted the selfishness of husbands and the resulting indifference of wives, without guidance regarding the sexual relationship. Therefore, he issued reminders to men about women's sexual capacity and the way in which women experience pleasure. The hadith reported by Abu Ya'la tells husbands that they should consider their wife's sexual fulfilment alongside their own each time sex occurs. The hadith reported by Dailami places the onus on the husband to make this happen and his inability to do so is characterised as a male weakness. Both hadiths call upon the husband to take the lead in making marital sex mutually satisfying; not by assuming he knows best or imposing his preconceived notions about sex, but by proactively engaging the wife in a combined effort at learning and enhancing their mutual enjoyment.

If the male believer is to take the woman-specific sexual hadiths as legally enforceable, they should take the hadiths directed at men as legal injunctions to satisfy their wives every time they have sex, without fail and without excuses. By looking at the two categories of sexual hadiths side-by-side, a man's duty to fulfil his wife's satisfaction every time they have sex effectively cancels out his purported

SEX, SOUL AND ISLAM

right to demand sex. This is because, in reality, no woman can possibly be sexually aroused, let alone satisfied, through involuntarily sex – be it by the moral threat of cursing angels, legal enforcement of rights or use of physical violence.

Therefore, the misogynistic, abusive, male-centric reading of conjugal rights cannot be attributed to any of these hadiths. The real reason behind the sexual machismo we see in the Muslim community, past and present, is the obsessive focus by men on the Prophet's advice to women while ignoring the guidance for men. Turning the woman-specific hadiths into legislation in some Muslim jurisdictions is yet another manifestation of such selective interpretations.

Dealing With Sexual Hadiths

Not every hadith of the Prophet ﷺ must be taken as an enforceable legal proclamation. Nor can every family issue be resolved through such legislation. Misappropriation of the sexual hadiths leads to the type of legal short-circuit we have seen above. This is because sex is a complex, delicate and intimate issue. It is a physio-psycho-emotional experience and any problems arising from it are best resolved through a meeting of the hearts rather than a prescribed list of rights and wrongs. It is far better for a mutually satisfying sexual relationship between husband and wife if these hadiths are regarded more as moral guidance than legal precepts.

Interestingly, from our own encounters with qualified lawyers, arbitrators and judges of the *Syariah* Court in Singapore, we observe that the legally trained are more circumspect in dealing with such hadiths. Many of them would advise that sex-related issues are better dealt with by marriage counsellors working together with the couples, than through dispensing legal judgments on who is right or wrong in conjugal disputes. They know that law is only an instrument of justice and in marital disputes, legal positions are easily blurred by complex and ever-changing real-life circumstances and inter-personal dynamics. It is those who delude themselves as *fuqaha* (experts in Islamic jurisprudence) without any real training or knowledge, who are most obstinate about their purported rights and their spouses' purported violations of them.

In our many years of experience, we have only come across husbands arming themselves with hadiths in order to intimidate their wives during counselling. We suspect that is because most wives are ignorant of the sexual hadiths espousing the rights of women. We do not wish that after reading this book, wives will be arming themselves with such hadiths in a similar fashion. Nor do we believe it was the Prophet's intention for couples to use his warnings as weapons against each other. The Prophet ﷺ was not a sex therapist. His advice was meant for the masses.

Mutuality, reciprocity and **equitability** seem to be largely **missing** from sociological observations of Muslim sexual **mores**, both past and **present**.

Therefore, he employed adequately strong linguistic devices to emphasise the seriousness of each spouse's individual sexual responsibility to the other. We must be wise in dealing with these public proclamations so as to enhance, not jeopardise our sexual experience.

To illustrate by comparison, the Quran equally proclaims God's mercy as well as His punishments, but whether these verses are beneficial to you or not, depends on your wisdom in focusing on the right verses at the right time. For example, when we are tempted to sin, verses concerning God's punishment will stop us in our tracks, whereas focusing on His forgiveness may persuade us to sin first and repent later. Conversely, when contemplating repentance, verses extolling God's mercy will encourage us whereas those concerning punishment may lead us to believe that repentance is futile.

Similarly, both the man and woman specific sexual hadiths are available to both parties to contemplate and reflect upon. It is wisest for wives to take heed of the sexual hadiths that speak directly to them and respond positively to their husbands' sexual advances. Likewise, it is wisest that husbands focus on the man-specific narrations that place the onus on them to create a mutually satisfying sexual atmosphere at home. As with all other marital matters, the husbands' leadership is crucial – but not leadership by commandment and certainly not by force. It is leadership by example that is needed here. That requires him to understand his wife better – what she looks for in sex, what turns her on, what keeps her aroused and what it takes to satisfy her fully. What attracts a wife most is a husband who understands, empathises with and cares about her condition and welfare over and above his own. Paradoxically, to such a husband she will surrender her mind and body without threats of cursing angels, enforcement orders, physical force or emotional coercion. Then, when both parties are keen on pleasing each other, they are better placed to appreciate the final category of sexual hadiths directed at couples.

> Let none of you fall suddenly upon his wife like an animal. Let there be a
> messenger between the two. Someone asked: 'What is the messenger,
> O Prophet?' He said: 'Kissing and words of love.'
>
> (Dailami)

In this hadith, the Prophet ﷺ calls upon Muslims to look beyond the *sharia* of sex towards embracing its *akhlaq*, that is the refinement of sexual conduct so that it is not akin to that of an animal. Refined sex between humans is more than the intercourse of genitals for reproduction, sexual release or any other purely animalistic function. The scope of sexual pleasure is expanded beyond the carnal to encompass the human senses, emotions and imagination, leading to a perfect communion of two people involving every aspect of their humanity – including but not limited to the pleasures of the flesh.

In conclusion, the sexual hadiths are best dealt with in their entirety and viewed as moral guidance, to develop our sexual *akhlaq* i.e. to refine our sexual conduct. This shall be explored further in the next chapter. For now, we will remain with the *sharia* of sex to address one of the most extreme manifestations of the male-biased interpretation of conjugal rights – the supposed legality of marital rape.

Conjugal Rights and Marital Rape

Marital rape occurs when one spouse uses force to obtain sexual gratification from the other – usually the husband over the wife. It is controversial because rape, by definition is non-consensual sex involving emotional or physical coercion and is universally considered a punishable crime whereas marriage in all religions and cultures as well as secularistic charters, guarantees the conjugal rights of husbands and wives. Thus, it has long been maintained that rape – which is non-consensual sex – cannot happen in marriage as both parties implicitly consented to sex at the point of solemnisation. For that reason, throughout much of human history, sexual violence inflicted by husbands on their wives has been exempted from the legal definition of rape as an otherwise punishable crime. Even in the countries where marital rape is now illegal, it was not recognised as such until the mid-20th century.

While it is not a problem unique to us, many Muslim countries are still failing to illegalise marital rape as they are unsure if it is really wrong. To regard it as such threatens the marital guarantee of conjugal rights which undeniably must be preserved if marriage is to retain its original meaning and importance in Islamic life. This is an unfortunate digression from the real issue behind marital rape and will remain a sticking point if we keep pitting the non-consensual nature of rape against the implicit consent to sex given at the point of marriage. Instead, we should be looking at:

a)   the husband's lawful right to sex against
b)   his lawful means of recourse when his right is violated

A **husband's right to sex** with his wife is ensured by Islam. When a wife refuses to have sex with her husband – without valid grounds recognised by Islam – the wife has indeed breached her marital vows and the husband's right has been violated. However, the husband's **means of recourse** are not open to his whims and fancies. It is governed by *sharia*. Marital counselling, sex therapy, termination of marriage and polygamy (if the husband is worthy) are just some of the means of recourse sanctioned by *sharia*, but it has never sanctioned physical force and psychological coercion – for that matter, drugging, hypnotism, court order or any other enforcement methods – as means of recourse for restoring the sexual rights of a husband. Thus, a husband cannot claim to have an Islamically sanctioned right to force himself onto his unwilling wife just because he has a right to sexual gratification. Even if his wife has failed him, his means of recourse is governed by marital laws in Islam, which does not include violence and coercion.

In fact, if rape is defined as sexual intercourse without consent, rape can actually happen in marriage even if the marital vow is an implicit blanket consent for sexual intercourse, because when a wife refuses to have sex with her husband, she has in effect withdrawn that consent from her husband for reasons she knows best. The "victimised" husband has lawful means of recompense as a consequence of her action, but that is subject to a judicial process, be it on Earth or on the Day of Judgment. Either way, the husband does not have any right to inflict his own version of punishment nor to reclaim his right from his wife in whatever way he wishes.

It is not uncommon for marital rape to be justified on grounds of wife discipline using the Quranic verse, *Al-Nisa 4:34:*

> ... *But those [wives] from whom you fear arrogance - [first] advise them;*
> *[then if they persist], forsake them in bed; and [finally],* **strike them** ...
> (Al-Nisa 4:34)

This is a cynical, self-serving abuse of the husbandly authority placed by Allah ﷻ on men. Forcing sex onto an unwilling wife is a direct violation of the Prophet's order to men not to copulate with their wives like animals. For a man to "fall suddenly upon his wife" (Dailami) violates the Islamic concept of *akhlaq* (refined conduct). Imagine then, how much worse the violation is when it is accompanied by physical injury and psychological trauma. Furthermore, *Al-Nisa 4:34*, as with any other Quranic injunction, should be coherently implemented from the beginning to the end, starting with admonition to sexual withdrawal to the option to "strike (the wife)". **Even if** its superficial literal meaning is taken, the "strike them" course of action should not lead to forced sex as it will effectively undo the second step in this process – that is sexual withdrawal. Thus, when considered as a coherent process, *Al-Nisa 4:34* is really a poor excuse for justifying marital rape.

Let us explore this verse further. *Al-Nisa 4:34* specifies that the process of responding to a wife's problematic behaviour begins with admonition and that requires a proper understanding of the subject at hand, as a prerequisite. With regards to sexual rejection, it has much less to do with sexual conditions than inter-personal differences in preferences, tastes, expectations, temperament, adventurism, health and welfare as well as the general sense of satisfaction within the wider marital relationship. Cases of sexual refusal cannot be solved by force nor by enforcement. Instead, both parties need expert admonition in the form of sexual therapy or marital counselling or both, if they truly want to solve their collective problem. The judicial process is only relevant if the couple has decided to part ways in a just and peaceful manner.

Therefore, neither verse *Al-Nisa 4:34* nor the universal definition of conjugal rights in marriage can justify a husband's use of force for sexual gratification. The controversy around marital rape is perpetuated by the erroneous assumption that it is a conflict between the non-consensual nature of rape and the implicit consent of marriage. More relevant to the issue is the fact that marital conjugal rights do not come with enforcement rights. Instead, aggrieved parties must seek recourse through the process of law to ensure justice to both parties. Thus, marital rape happens when a husband takes the law into his own hands and enforces his will on his wife with violence. It is a crime that should be treated as severely as any other form of rape.

Al-Nisa 4:34 and Wife-Beating

This would be a good juncture at which to discuss wife-beating as, in many cases domestic violence and marital rape come hand in hand. Ironically, it is a problem which both Muslim chauvinists and Islamophobes attribute to Islam, but in reality, domestic abuse is a global issue affecting every society including Muslim communities. Islam's detractors seek to use the topic of domestic abuse to discredit Islam and this is helped in no small part by misogynistic legal systems in certain Muslim countries and quack *imams* insisting on men's so-called divine right to discipline wives with physical punishments.

Armed with English translations of the Quran and hadiths, so many modern critics of Islam flood the internet with their theories that wife-beating is prescribed by the Quran and was practised by the Prophet ﷺ. So many websites insist that since the verse, *Al-Nisa 4:34* commands Muslims to "strike (their wives)", it is a disciplinary measure which is not only accepted, but encouraged by the Holy Book. Admittedly, a significant number of classical Muslim scholars expressed such sentiments too, providing fodder for this assertion. In fact, you can find modern examples even from Muslim women influencers repeating such classical views[36] alongside the contemporary male voices. Be that as it may, to have a proper understanding of the issue of wife-beating, we must relook at all the Quranic verses and hadiths regarding it.

SEX, SOUL AND ISLAM

Then, instead of taking one single verse in isolation, all sources must be analysed holistically in conjunction with the overall message of Islam, socio-historical context and taking into account the authenticity of the hadiths used.

O you who have believed, it is not lawful for you to inherit women by compulsion... And live with them in kindness ...
(Al-Nisa 4:19)

Do not beat Allah's handmaidens.

(Abu Dawud)

Mu'awiyah al-Qushayri narrated: "I went to the Apostle of Allah (peace be upon him) and asked him: 'What do you say (command) about our wives?' He replied: 'Give them food of what you have for yourself, and clothe them by which you clothe yourself, and do not beat them, and do not revile them.'"

(Baihaqi)

The best of you are those who are the best to their women.

(Tirmidhi)

The phrase "strike them" is indeed found in verse *Al-Nisa 4:34* as translated from the Arabic command "*idhribu hunna*". However, Arabic is precise and in this form it refers to a single beating whereas the command for multiple beating would be "*dharribu hunna*". At the same time, a hadith limits the instrument of beating to no bigger than a twig.[37] Putting the two together, the idea of physically attacking a wife in a way that will cause serious harm to her cannot be attributed to this verse, as it refers to a single symbolic strike which is not intended to hurt her. Therefore, this command actually serves no purpose for either the pro or anti-wife beating camps. A symbolic strike does not ensure a wife's obedience as those who are in favour would claim, nor can it discourage beating among the latter because whether single or multiple strikes are used, beating is beating.

Any verse must be studied within the context of Islam's wider notions of kindness towards women as practised by the Prophet ﷺ who, as well as treating his own wives and daughters with love and tenderness, spent a lifetime establishing and protecting the rights of women, whether it was abolishing female infanticide and levirate marriage[38] or introducing women's rights to inheritance and divorce. Therefore, to obtain a clearer understanding of *Al-Nisa 4:34*, we need to look beyond

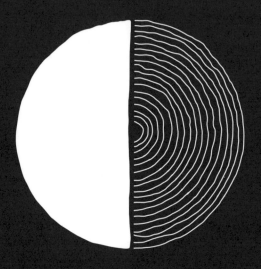

Ironically, Muslim male **chauvinists** are united with **Islamophobes** in using **certain** hadiths to insist that Islam sanctions **male** chauvinism to the point of sexual **coercion**.

its literal meaning.

The late Ustaz Abdillah Aljufri, a prominent Islamic teacher in Singapore, explained it as an effective necessary limit to the prevalent ill-treatment suffered by women at the time of the Prophet ﷺ.[39] To completely ban the physical "disciplining" of wives in the early days of Islam would have been rejected by an extremely patriarchal society in which a culture of misogyny was deeply ingrained. Instead, the Prophet's approach was more pragmatic. Permission was given for the symbolic strike which both appeased men who believed they were still maintaining a semblance of control and protected women from more serious violence.

In addition, by simultaneously speaking out against wife-beating while promoting kindness towards women, the Messenger of Allah ﷺ set into motion gradual societal changes in the treatment of women. Thus "strike them" should not be seen as the preferred disciplinary measure to be used against wives today or worse still, as justification for domestic violence. It was a necessary limit for society at that time and it should not even be an option in contemporary Muslim society. With better education, awareness and acceptance of gender equity, our communities are more than ready to embrace the long-term Islamic goal of kindness in marital relationships.

The gradual approach towards change is a common feature in Islam. Other social problems like alcoholism, gambling, usury and adultery were also outlawed gradually through discouragements to conditional allowances to a complete ban when conditions were right during the Prophet's lifetime. Misogyny and slavery[40] are examples of the deeper ingrained social ills that required longer than his lifetime to abolish.

Some hadiths and verses of the Quran which allude to this measured process in order for later generations to understand the necessity for gradualism are open to manipulation by those with vested interests, to suggest Islam's regression towards the very social ills it set out to abolish. That is what has happened with *Al-Nisa 4:34* and with the following hadith:

> *Abdullah bin Abu Dhubab reported the Apostle of Allah ﷺ as saying:*
> *"Do not beat Allah's handmaidens", but when Umar came to the Apostle*
> *of Allah ﷺ and said: "Women have become emboldened towards their*
> *husbands", he (the Prophet ﷺ) gave permission to beat them. Then*
> *many women came around the family of the Apostle of Allah ﷺ with*
> *complaints against their husbands. So the Apostle of Allah ﷺ said:*
> *"Many women have approached Muhammad's family complaining*
> *about their husbands. They are not the best amongst you."*
>
> (Abu Dawud)

This hadith has been used to argue that the Prophet ﷺ changed his mind about wife-beating when pressured by Umar ؓ and confirmed that u-turn by criticising the women who came to him complaining about being beaten. Hence, the seed of wife-beating as an Islamic cultural norm was germinated.

In reality, this incident captured exactly the gradual process mentioned above. The Prophet's standing order was, "Do not beat Allah's handmaidens". Umar's appeal and the complaints of the wives reflected a brewing 'battle of the sexes' following the Prophet's revolutionary call against wife-beating. The Prophet's allowance appeased the men and protected the women, as with the case of *Al-Nisa 4:34*. When some men failed to comply and their wives complained, he admonished the men, "They (the heavy-beating husbands) are not the best among you (men)". The Arabic text of this last statement used the masculine plural form for both the words "they" and "you" making it crystal clear that the Prophet ﷺ was in fact criticising the men for their violence and not their wives for complaining.

> The Prophet ﷺ said, "None of you should flog his wife as he flogs a slave and then have sexual intercourse with her in the last part of the day."
>
> (Bukhari)

> How does anyone of you beat his wife as he beats the stallion camel and then he may embrace (sleep with) her?...
>
> (Bukhari)

The above hadiths have also been used to illustrate that wife-beating is allowed by the Prophet ﷺ as long as it is not on the same level as flogging a slave or beating a stallion camel. In reality, the Prophet ﷺ was merely using figures of speech to paint a disgusting image of domestic abuse. When you are told not to be as stubborn as a mule, surely it does not mean you can be stubborn like any other animal, does it?

> (The Prophet's wife, Aishah ؓ) said: "... He struck me on the chest which caused me pain, and then said: Did you think that Allah and His Apostle would deal unjustly with you?"
>
> (Muslim)

This hadith is quoted in order to justify violence towards wives as *sunna* and therefore permissible. The incident is said to have occurred on a night when Aisha ؓ found the Prophet ﷺ missing from bed, grew suspicious and went out to look for him. She found him praying for the dead in the cemetery. Upon returning home, he noticed she was panting heavily and asked why. She told him of her spying and then what she reported above took place. In this report, she does not use the blessed word *"dharaba"* (strike) but *"lahada"* (pushed, shoved) instead. Nevertheless, she felt pain.

If we study the narration more closely though, it becomes apparent that the push was more likely a spontaneous reaction to Aisha's doubts, than a pre-meditated act of violence. Given that she was fatigued and out of breath, the push may have caused more pain than the Prophet 🕌 realised. Indeed, if Aisha 🕌 herself had understood the Prophet's actions to be intended as a beating she would not have declared that, "Allah's Messenger 🕌 never hit anything with his hand ever... Nor did he ever hit a servant or a woman" (Ibn Majah).

Another hadith which is interpreted as Islam permitting domestic abuse is narrated by Umar ibn al-Khattab and purports, "The Prophet 🕌 said, 'A man will not be asked as to why he beat his wife'" (Abu Dawud). Firstly, the fact that the words are that of the Prophet 🕌 suggests that the beating is the symbolic "strike" referred to in the Quran and in keeping with the advice the Prophet 🕌 gives in other narrations. Secondly, "a man will not be asked" could well be interpreted as meaning that the man who beats his wife will be swiftly punished by Allah 🕌 regardless of why he has lashed out. Finally, and most importantly, this hadith was classified as *dhaif* or weak by all its compilers and therefore, cannot be used to support the validity of wife-beating in Islam. This is an established legal precept in Islamic jurisprudence.

Some may ask why – if Islam is so opposed to domestic abuse – did the Prophet 🕌 not punish abusers publicly, delivering a clear message of zero-tolerance? It is easy to reach this conclusion as a twenty-first century critic, when much of the groundwork against misogyny has already been painstakingly laid by earlier reformers, including the Prophet 🕌, but when we take into account the socio-historical context, can we honestly say we would have done things differently? Gender equality was an unthinkable notion in seventh century Arabia. Despite this, the Messenger of Allah 🕌 had already instigated meaningful change in the area of women's rights, but the incident involving Umar 🕌 and the women of Medina which we discussed earlier in this section is proof that the road to abolishing thousands of years of male dominance and female subjugation was a long one. Recognising this, the Prophet 🕌 wisely employed a strategy of patience, choosing to introduce reforms in a way that ensured they would be fully absorbed into the fabric of society. We can perpetuate the Prophet's legacy by consigning all forms of wife-beating to history and embracing his ultimate wish for "tranquillity, love and mercy" in our marital relationships.

There is no absolute consensus among Muslims concerning the issue of wife-beating. Nor do we have illusions that the gradualism theory we have explored will be accepted by everyone who reads it. Unfortunately, this contention among us has been used by the sizeable online industry dedicated to discrediting Islam, using the issue of wife-beating as their favourite weapon. Their manipulation of the Quran and hadiths and the erroneous and biased interpretations of Muslim influencers who are still justifying wife-beating in this day and age, work hand-in-hand to present Islam as a misogynistic and oppressive religion. As marital counsellors, we see the detrimental effect this has on Muslim women and by extension, their marriages.

Discrediting Islam will not help abused wives who, despite all their suffering, are unlikely to accept support from those who disparage their faith. There are many Muslim voices discrediting wife-beating, marital rape and other forms of misogyny. It is more productive to familiarise all Muslim women – whether they are victims of abuse or not – with their right to be treated equally as their religion demands. With that, we turn back our attention to conjugal rights to conclude our study on how Quranic verses and prophetic examples can be misinterpreted and exploited away from their intended purpose.

Re-understanding Conjugal Rights

For much of human history, the balance of power between the genders has never been equal. Sadly, the dominion of men over women has been a common trait amongst communities around the world since ancient times. Much of the time, this domination has centred around sex. With the growing awareness of gender equality at the turn of the twentieth century, the rights of women to work, own property and vote were won. In the 1960s there also emerged a movement for equal opportunity in sexual gratification.

The sexual revolution promoted women's right to have sex as much and as often as they like, even outside of marriage, without being socially reproached – an immunity men have always enjoyed. By the 1980s, many women growing up post-revolution found that it improved little in the way of women's sexual contentment because much of what went on in the bedroom was still dictated by men and their sexual preferences. Instead, the revolution also gave rise to a growing social pressure for women to be sexually adventurous and satisfy the more base desires of men in the process.[41] With hindsight, we can see that the sexual revolution has not delivered on the promise of a truly mutually shared sexual experience between the genders.

The subjugation of women through sex has also caused many problems in the Islamic world through history and still hinders the progress of our communities today. In the case of marriage, the Islamic concept of conjugal rights is abused to justify this oppression. How unfortunate that this concept of mutually guaranteed

The real reason behind the sexual machismo we see in the Muslim community, past and present, is the obsessive focus by men on the Prophet's advice to women while ignoring the guidance for men.

conjugal rights has been misused to ensure a man's sexual domination in marriages, rather than a mutually shared bliss. Ironically, even if gender equality is achieved, the concept of conjugal rights and the lack of understanding surrounding it, may still be a stumbling block to the type of sexual experience as envisaged in *Al-Rum 30:21*. We say this on reflection of some of the cases we, as counsellors, have been privy to. These cases relate to an interesting development in the Muslim community's changing perception about sex.

There is a growing awareness of equal conjugal rights between husband and wife as taught in Islam, with many Islamic websites, blogs and books reminding husbands of their wives' rights in accordance with the Quran and Sunna. Yet, in counselling, we have come across husbands who are annoyed, not by their wives demanding sexual rights, but by their lack of enthusiasm in pursuing those rights.

One husband could not understand why his wife would continually refuse his sexual advances even as she reminded him of her sexual needs. The wife too was confused because in the scheme of sexual justice she agreed she was depriving both herself and her husband of their rights. Despite this, she argued that her conjugal rights should also include the right to refuse sex especially when her husband's perception of sexual enjoyment was so different to her own. The husband insisted that she would eventually enjoy intercourse if they persisted in practicing, but in her mind, every "practice" session was bringing her further away from her expectation of what sex should be.

This example illustrates how obsessing over conjugal rights can potentially lead to conjugal stalemates. Whilst it is important to be aware of conjugal rights in order to avoid such problems as sexual domination, especially when violence is involved, viewing those rights solely as an enforceable contract is also a hindrance to sexual and marital bliss. The concept of conjugal rights has long been viewed as the right to **get sex from** each other – in the sense of a contract which both parties must honour. However, it can also be viewed as "the right to **have sex with** each other" – in the sense of a privilege granted by God exclusively to a husband and wife. By understanding marriage and conjugal rights as a God-given privilege instead of a legally drawn contract, sex will not be reduced to a matter of duties, responsibilities or entitlements but will blossom from desire, seduction, love and pleasure.

Islam recognises conjugal rights as both contract and privilege, through the lenses of *sharia* (law) and *akhlaq* (refined conduct) respectively. One is about getting your rights, the other about getting it right. Law delineates basic requirements and boundary markers. It is a good viewpoint from which to understand one's minimum responsibilities, but you may also choose to surpass the basic expectations and reach for the higher virtues that any law aspires towards. In the case of sexual laws, tranquillity, love and mercy between couples. By doing so, Muslims are observing the *sharia* in a way which is true to its essence.

By viewing conjugal rights as a privilege, couples will find that sex occurs naturally and voluntarily. There are no guarantees, no sense of entitlement. Instead, lovers must woo each other. The focus is shifted to pleasure and satisfaction, rather than compulsion. In order to enjoy sex as the privilege it is, couples must understand that even differences in sexual perceptions are a source of strength, interest and variety, instead of friction. Through this understanding, husband and wife can spend a lifetime together learning, honing skills, communicating and attending to each other to ensure that the sex remains beautiful. Obtaining sex through force or legislations is the lazy, selfish and ignorant route and will not lead to sexual fulfilment. Good sex cannot be forced or legislated but must be nurtured and cultivated like all other aspects of human relationships.

Thus, we shall revisit this topic in Chapter 4: The Sexual Experience which deals with relational aspects of sexual activity. Among others, we also elaborate the "messenger" concept and the practical difference between male and female sexual arousal which we mentioned many times above. But before that, let's look in Chapter 3, at a number of prescribed rulings and etiquettes, starting from some classically categorised issues up to contemporary sexual hang-ups and shenanigans which are challenging these categorisations. It gives us an opportunity to illustrate that above all, Quranic ideals guide the formation of these rulings and etiquettes. Particularly relevant in most of these is the concept of exclusive zones for sexual indulgences, an ideal we discussed thoroughly in Chapter 1.

Conclusion

Laws on conjugal rights are meant to remind and guide couples towards observing their mutual responsibilities in ensuring each other's satisfaction and happiness, but they only work to that effect if they are understood and observed comprehensively, with each gender fulfilling their own requirements, instead of obsessing over the other's responsibilities. There is also a balance to be struck between following the letter of the law in regards to conjugal duties and imbibing the spirit of the law through the way we conduct ourselves around our partner. Only when that balance is achieved, can couples enjoy a mutually blissful union involving every aspect of their humanity.

In three matters, the weakness of a male is expressed
... (thirdly) the man who approaches his wife and
thereby fulfils his (sexual) desire from her before she
fulfilled hers from him.

DAILAMI

Chapter 3
Rulings and Etiquettes of Sex

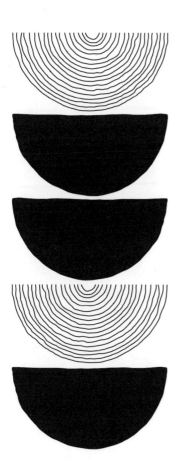

The primary sources of Islamic guidance are the Quran and the Prophet Muhammad's examples. From these, Muslim scholars have developed a system of jurisprudence *(fiqh)* to guide the general Muslim public on the practical implementation of their responsibilities. Similarly, for the continual development of character, moral precepts known as *adab* or etiquettes direct them on the finer points of appropriate behaviour. This compilation of rulings and etiquettes is an important foundation for a sexual relationship, keeping us grounded in Islamic values as we trawl through multiple sources of knowledge concerning sex in our quest to enrich our sexual experience.

For easy reference and implementable guidance, the rulings and etiquettes concerning sex are expressed in the following terms: *wajib* (obligatory), sunna (recommended), *makruh* (undesirable), *mubah* (legally neutral) and *haram* (forbidden). In practical terms, the rulings guide couples to maximise sexual enjoyment while protecting them from potential breaches of the laws surrounding this exclusive privilege. In addition, it keeps their sexual activities consistent with other aspects of the teachings of Islam.

Obligatory (*wajib*)

When sex is obligatory: Implicit within the marital vows is the understanding that both husband and wife have a duty to satisfy each other's sexual desires. However, there are specific reminders to both parties that take into account the different natures of men and women.

Men are reminded that their duty to provide maintenance to their wives includes sexual 'maintenance'. Thus, the principles of generosity, regularity and promptness in financial maintenance should also figure as important criteria in satisfying their wives' sexual desires. This serves to address men's tendency to neglect their wives' sexual satisfaction due to the more reserved nature of women in expressing their sexual needs.

In turn, wives are reminded to be sensitive to their husbands' sexual advances which are typically more frequent due to men's sexual forthrightness. Frequent refusals or flippant dismissals can give rise to negative feelings which affect the entire marital relationship. Hence, you will find such hadiths:

> When a man invites his wife to his bed and she does not come, and he
> (the husband) spends the night being angry with her, the angels curse
> her until morning.
>
> (Muslim)

If a man calls his wife, then let her come, even if she is busy at the oven.

(Tirmidhi)

If a man calls his wife to his bed, let her respond, even if she is riding her camel [i.e. very busy].

(al-Bazzar)

The two sets of reminders must be taken in combination to refer to a married couple's conjugal responsibility to each other. Islam regards sexual satisfaction as a key element in the marital contract, such that failure to fulfil one's responsibilities is accepted as grounds for divorce. However, laws provide extreme limits of permissibility and are meant to protect the rights of a victimised party. Couples should strive to create a healthy sexual relationship based on consultation and communication.

A husband should remember that it is his overall duty to treat his wife with kindness. There may be times when he will have to find a balance between demanding his right to be sexually satisfied and his duty to be sensitive to his wife's feelings. A wife, on the other hand, may at times have to consider sacrificing her own comfort to attend to her husband's needs. In being kind and considerate of each other, they should avoid flexing their 'legal rights' for sexual access as this normally gives rise to further dissatisfaction and ill-feeling. Instead, they should embrace the spirit behind conjugal rights rulings, which is mutual bliss

The bath is compulsory after sex: "When a man sits in between the four parts of a woman and engages in sexual intercourse with her, the bath becomes compulsory, even if he does not ejaculate" (Bukhari). After sexual intercourse, the couple must perform the compulsory major ablution known as *ghusl*, before performing certain devotional acts such as reading the Quran, praying or entering the mosque. *Ghusl* is a physical purification meant to psychologically prepare us for the act of spiritual purification. Symbolically, it serves as a transition from an intense physical activity to a spiritual one. Practically, it is an appropriate refreshment after sex. There are two criteria for the compulsory bath:

- To have the intention of performing *ghusl*, for example by saying in your heart, "I am performing the compulsory bath because of Allah ﷻ" at the beginning of *ghusl*.
- To cleanse the whole body with water.

Ablution may be performed in the following manner, as reported by the Prophet's wife, Aisha ؓ:

Whenever the Prophet of Allah took the bath of janaba (state of major ritual impurity resulting from sexual intercourse or seminal discharge), he cleaned his hands and performed ablution like that for prayer and then took a bath and rubbed his hair till he felt that the whole skin of the head had become wet. Then we would pour water thrice and wash the rest of the body.

(Bukhari)

Decency and privacy during sex: Decency and privacy should be emphasised at certain times of the day and under certain circumstances. This is intended for when there are other people, particularly children in the home. The Quran gives guidance in this matter:

O you who have believed, let those whom your right hands possess and those who have not [yet] reached puberty among you ask permission of you [before entering] at three times: before the dawn prayer and when you put aside your clothing [for rest] at noon and after the night prayer. [These are] three times of privacy for you. There is no blame upon you nor upon them beyond these [periods], for they continually circulate among you - some of you, among others. Thus does Allah make clear to you the verses; and Allah is Knowing and Wise.

(Al-Nur 24:58)

Another verse instructs families to teach their children to ask permission before entering the parents' bedroom:

And when the children among you reach puberty, let them ask permission [at all times] as those before them have done. Thus does Allah make clear to you His verses; and Allah is Knowing and Wise.

(Al-Nur 24:59)

Exposure of the naked body to others, except spouses, is highly prohibited in Islam, such that even our own children are to be excluded. In relation to this, there is an oft quoted hadith against being stark naked, even between spouses, "When any of you approaches his wife, use covers and do not be naked like two asses" (Ibn Majah). However, this hadith is classified as weak and as with all weak hadiths, it cannot be a basis for any ruling, meaning spouses being naked together in a private and secure room is neither prohibited nor undesirable. Neither are blankets

SEX, SOUL AND ISLAM

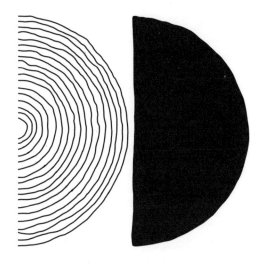

There may be times when a husband
will have to find a **balance**
between **demanding** his right
to be sexually **satisfied** and his
duty to be **sensitive** to his
wife's feelings.

compulsory nor recommended for lovemaking. In other words, the use of blankets is legally neutral. You can make love under covers if you choose to as it does have its advantages, for example if you feel more confident with the extra layer of privacy it provides. Religiously, it is considered *fadhail a'mal* or a virtuous act, but ignoring it is not blameworthy if you have other means of ensuring privacy.

Confidentiality of sexual matters: Safeguarding the privacy of your married life is compulsory. Revealing the intimate details and secrets of your marriage or the shortcomings of your spouse to others, even in jest, is strongly condemned. The Prophet ﷺ warned, "Among those who will have the worst position in Allah's sight on the Day of Resurrection is the man who has intercourse with his wife, and she with him, and then spreads her secret" (Muslim).[42] This is in line with the concept of marriage as a safe and exclusive psycho-emotional environment where the most intimate of pleasures can be explored.

Recommended (*sunna*)

When sex is recommended: It is recommended that couples have sexual inter-course on Friday or the night before (Thursday night). Friday is considered a week-end holiday in the Islamic calendar, but remember, this is only a suggested practice. It does not mean that making love on other days is unfavourable. It it is meant as a form of celebration on a holy day implied by hadiths like this, "Whoever comes on Friday, then let him perform *ghusl*" (Tirmidhi).

The Prophet's hygienic habits: It was the *sunna* of the Prophet ﷺ to take his ablution *(wudu)* prior to having sex with his wife. He would also clean his teeth and use perfume. Taking this cue, couples should groom and perfume themselves for each other as their good looks are meant for each other's admiration and not others. Hence, they should aspire to look their best at home, more than for work or attending public functions. We have discussed above that it is compulsory to take an obligatory bath after sexual intercourse. In addition, it is recommended to wash the genitals and take ablution before engaging in another round of sexual intercourse.

Importance of dua (supplication): As sex is viewed as a gift from Allah ﷻ, He should not be absent from our minds during the act. In fact, the Prophet ﷺ promoted a number of duas which remind us of our reliance on Him to give us the benefits of sex and to protect us from any possible harm. Certain companions of the Prophet ﷺ, including Abdullah Ibn Mas'ud ﷺ and Abu Dhar ﷺ, recommended two *raka'at* (cycles of prayer) to be performed together on the first night of sexual union. This is to be done like the Subh prayer (but without the *qunut*). At the beginning of the prayer, you should make your intention to worship Allah ﷻ in appreciation of His gift of the marriage. Then, after the prayer, this supplication is recommended:

"O Allah, bless me through my family and bless them through me. O Allah, bring us together in a good union and if you are to separate us, separate us towards good."[43]

In one narration, the Prophet ﷺ recommended that the husband touch the wife's forehead and supplicate to Allah ﷻ for blessings[44]. An example of a suitable dua to be made at this point is, "O Allah! Bless me with her affection and her acceptance of me; and make me pleased with her and bring us together in the best form of union and in absolute harmony; surely you like what is lawful and dislike the unlawful things," and the following dua can be recited before sexual intercourse:

> *If any one of you, when having sexual intercourse with his wife says:*
> *"Bismillah, Allahumma Jannibna Minash Shaithaan Wa Jannibish*
> *Shaithaana Ma Razaaqtana (In the Name of Allah! O Allah! Protect me*
> *from Shaitan and protect what you have bestowed upon us i.e. offspring,*
> *from Shaytan)" and it is destined that they should have a child, then*
> *Shaytan will never be able to harm him.*
>
> (Bukhari)

Forbidden (*haram*)

Menstruation and post-natal bleeding: In consideration of the discomfort experienced by a woman during menstruation and post-natal bleeding, Islam has forbidden sex on these occasions. Hygiene is also a consideration, as it is said in the Quran:

> *And they ask you about menstruation. Say, "It is harm, so keep away from wives*
> *during menstruation. And do not approach them until they are pure. And when*
> *they have purified themselves, then come to them from where Allah has ordained*
> *for you. Indeed, Allah loves those who are constantly repentant and loves those*
> *who purify themselves."*
> (Al-Baqarah 2:222)

However, this prohibition only refers to sexual acts involving penetration. Other kinds of sensual and sexual pleasing need not cease during menstruation as is made clear from the example of Allah's Messenger ﷺ, "Whenever the Prophet ﷺ desires something (sexual) from his wife who has her menses, he will place something (cloth) to cover her private organs" (Muslim).

The duration of menstruation has been given by many scholars to be between one and fifteen days. If it lasts for less than one, or for more than fifteen days, it is considered *istihazah* (irregular bleeding) and intercourse is permissible after the woman has cleansed herself, but this is a general guide. A more reliable measure can be gained through close observation of the monthly cycle. This is derived from the Prophet's explanation to his wife Umm Salamah 🕮 concerning a woman with a prolonged flow of blood.

> *She should consider the number of nights and days during which she used to menstruate each month before she was afflicted with this trouble and abandon prayer during that period each month. When these days and nights are over, she should take a bath, tie a cloth around her private parts and pray.*

(Abu Dawud)

This also means that a woman may use more reliable methods of confirmation, if available. Women today can ask their doctor to help determine which bleeding is menstruation or post-natal bleeding and which is not. After either of these has ceased, the couple may resume sex after the woman has cleansed and bathed.

Fasting: During fasting, you not only have to abstain from food and drink, but must also refrain from having sexual intercourse. However, this is only during the fasting hours between dawn and dusk. You are free to have sex once the fast is broken. The Quran says:

> *It has been made permissible for you the night preceding fasting to go to your wives [for sexual relations]. They are a clothing for you and you are a clothing for them...*
> (Al-Baqarah 2:187)

Engaging in sex while fasting will nullify the fast. Additionally, the husband must pay *kafarah* (expiation) by fasting daily for two months consecutively or by feeding sixty poor people. The wife is exempted from this penalty.

Ihram during the pilgrimage: When performing the small pilgrimage *(umrah)* or pilgrimage *(hajj)* to Makkah, sex is forbidden when you are in the state of devotion *(ihram)*. Sex may be resumed after all the rites have been completed and you exit the state of devotion. Participation in any aspect of the marriage ceremony is also forbidden while in *ihram*.

Anal intercourse is forbidden: Islam absolutely forbids anal intercourse. The Prophet 🕮 said, "He who has intercourse with his wife through her anus is accursed" (Abu Dawud). Reports concerning sexual intercourse from the rear are not to be misconstrued as through the anus, as is clear from another hadith, "You may (have sexual intercourse) from the front or the rear, as long as it is in her vagina" (Bukhari).

SEX, SOUL AND ISLAM

Bestiality is forbidden: The use of animals for sexual gratification predates the coming of Islam. So, when Islam arrived, the Prophet ﷺ made it clear that it is *haram.* The only contention among scholars is with regards to its punishment.[45]

Undesirable (*makruh*)

Apart from the occasions outlined above where sex is *haram*, sexual intercourse is permissible in most other instances. Nonetheless, Islamic scholars have deemed it as undesirable in the following instances:

- During frightful natural occurrences such as an eclipse, earthquake or hurricane.
- When prayers are to be performed such as between dawn and sunrise, from sunset till *maghrib* and during special religious occasions like the eve of festivals such as Eid al-Fitr and Eid al-Adha.

These two examples suggest that sex is undesirable at times when participation in activities concerning the welfare or joy of the community are more important than an exclusive encounter with our spouses.

Legally neutral (*mubah*)

It is *mubah* to enjoy sexual intercourse in any position; be it the man above face-to-face, woman above face-to-face, side by side or even from the rear, so long as it is through the vagina. The Quran says:

> *Your wives are a place of cultivation [i.e. sowing of seed] for you, so come to your place of cultivation however you wish and put forth [righteousness] for yourselves. And fear Allah and know that you will meet Him. And give good tidings to the believers.*
> (Al-Baqarah 2:223)

The *sharia* allows couples to explore any position they wish as long as it suits them, does not cause discomfort, injury or health issues and is mutually satisfying or at least agreeable to both parties. For example, 'acrobatic positions' which may hurt and injure are discouraged.

Other than the above, there are many other sexual practices whose rulings are a little more complex than the clear cut *haram, sunna, wajib, makruh* or *mubah* categorisations. These were never addressed by the Prophet ﷺ specifically – either because they were non-issues during his lifetime, or nobody asked him about them.

The general rule in Islamic jurisprudence is that all things are permissible unless otherwise stated. However, when it comes to the following practices, it is the extent, manner and details of the practice which contradict well-established Islamic principles and values rather than the practice per se. So, their permissibility and decency are not universal but are rather couple-specific or situation-centric in nature.

Masturbation

Masturbation refers to self-stimulation of the genitals to the point of orgasm. There is no one definite legal ruling on masturbation as it was not mentioned explicitly in the Quran or Sunna. Different scholars have given very different opinions ranging from *haram* (forbidden) to *mubah* (neutral) as expounded by Sayyid Sabiq in his *Fiqhus Sunna.*[46] Despite this ambiguity, none of the jurists opined it was a punishable offence and all based their opinions on moral grounds.

> *Certainly will the believers have succeeded ... And they who guard their private parts except from their wives...*
> (Al-Mu'minun 23:1 ... 5, 6)

Those who believe it to be *haram* base their opinion on the above verse. With regards to masturbation, this verse is particularly relevant as it describes the characteristics of the "believers (who) have succeeded," in guarding their private parts from all except their spouse. Hence, the conclusion is that to attain sexual pleasure through one's own stimulation is forbidden for a believer.

Other scholars believe it to be forbidden in some circumstances, but compulsory in others; specifically, in circumstances that would result in a Muslim committing non-marital sex or *zina*. They base this opinion on the jurisprudence principle of choosing the lesser of two evils. An example they give is a person who can no longer contain their sexual desires and yet has no spouse to channel it towards. In such a case, it is permissible to relieve that tension through masturbation and compulsory if not doing so will lead to fornication.

Yet there are others who opine that masturbation is legally neutral. In other words, it is down to a person's discretion, but the circumstances in which they purport this discretion to be granted are involving war-time and youths – which still alludes to the principle of "the lesser of two evils."[47]

Although the stated opinions of the scholars seem to be at odds with one another, they all have one thing in common: exercising caution and reserving sexual enjoyment for legal partners as much as possible. They all regard masturbation only as a last resort to prevent the occurrence of fornication – as a means of sexual release rather than a source of enjoyment. But it must also be added that the Prophet's preferred remedy for control of sexual desires for unmarried people is fasting, "He who can afford to marry should marry, because it will help him refrain from looking at other women, and save his private parts from committing illegal sexual acts; and he who cannot afford to marry is advised to fast, as fasting will diminish his sexual power" (Bukhari).

What is not addressed in jurisprudence books is self-masturbation during sexual intercourse with a partner. A study recorded women using this strategy to achieve orgasm in lovemaking; be it during or out of intercourse, when the partner habitually fails to do so.[48] The ruling in such cases is the same: to regard it as a last resort to repel the temptations of fornication, but this is as far as rulings for the wife go. As for the husband, it is a case of him not fulfilling his conjugal responsibility. Muslim couples in such a situation must address the issue wisely and sensitively as this strategy can be alienating in the long run.

Partner masturbation, referring to pleasuring a partner with means other than intercourse, is another matter entirely. The Prophet's wife, Aisha 🕌 reported that, "Whenever the Prophet desires something (sexual) from his wife who has her menses, he will place something (cloth) to cover her private organs" (Muslim). This hadith alludes to the Prophet 🕌 fulfilling his sexual desires with his wives while avoiding their private organs which must mean that other parts of the body were involved instead. So, in general, non-coital sensual and sexual pleasuring is not an issue; except that when the mouth or foreign objects are used, other factors will determine its rulings. We discuss these next.

Oral Sex

Oral sex refers to the use of the mouth and its related parts like the tongue, lips, palette or throat – or even teeth, as far as definition goes – on parts of the body, especially the genitals, to stimulate or pleasure a partner. Specifically, when it is performed on female genitals, it is known as cunnilingus and on male genitals, fellatio. If masturbation is to be treated with caution because it excludes the spouse, oral sex is ordinarily impossible without a partner. So, what is its ruling among married couples?

Curiously enough, oral sex is not mentioned in the Quran or the sayings of the Prophet 🕌 although cunnilingus at least, was definitely known at that time. In one report, a companion of the Prophet 🕌 was recorded telling an idol-worshipper, "Go and suck the clitoris of al-Lat" – referring to the latter's goddess.[49] If it were undesirable or commendable on its own merit, the Prophet 🕌 would have declared it as being so and if his contemporaries had asked, his answer would surely have been recorded.

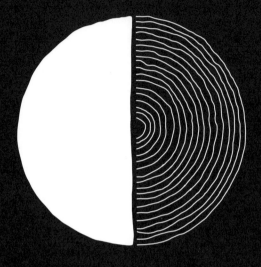

Scholars regard **masturbation** only as a **last resort** to prevent the occurrence of **fornication** – as a means of sexual **release** rather than a **source** of enjoyment.

Despite our best efforts, we could not find this ruling in modern compilations of classical jurisprudence including *Islamic Jurisprudence According To The Four Sunni schools* by Sheikh Abdul Rahman Jaziri (1941)[50] or *Fiqhus Sunna* by Sheikh Sayyid Sabiq (c 1945) and *The Lawful and the Prohibited in Islam* by Dr Yusuf Qaradawi (1960). Chances are, the four original imams of the Sunni schools of thought were never asked and thus never addressed the issue, even as they explained at length and in great detail about other sexual matters like fornication, masturbation, bestiality and homosexuality. In 2004, Dr Yusuf Al-Qaradawi was quoted as saying:

> *I was asked about oral sex in America and Europe when I began to travel to these countries in the early 70s. We are not used to being asked these questions in our Muslim countries ... These parts are not dirty like the anus, but it is ordinarily disgusting to man. But there is no decisive evidence to make it unlawful, especially if the wife agrees with it or achieves orgasm by practicing it.[51]*

By contrast, questions regarding oral sex are frequently asked by Muslims today and many online forums and websites address the topic. We find the comparison between the nonchalance of earlier Muslims and the curiosity of contemporary Muslims over oral sex rather intriguing and upon reflection, quite instructive. It cannot be due to Muslims in earlier times being unaware of the act of oral sex or being too shy to ask about it. More likely, it is because the way oral sex was perceived, approached and practised by those generations was very different to its portrayal in the pornography, erotic novels and scientifically researched sex books of today. Although they all fall under the rubric of "oral sex", the modern-day "deep throat ejaculation" fetish was most likely not what the 18th century Imam Murtadha Husaini Zabidi had in mind when he advised couples, "And approach intercourse with its preambles which is seducing with words and kissing on the cheeks and the lips to titillate the breasts and nipples and to stimulate every part of the body and loins."[52]

In the historic perception of oral sex among Muslims, it is an extension of sensual pleasuring which is a sunna we will discuss in Chapter Four. Since Islamic rulings and etiquette pertaining to handling of "body and loins" are clearly defined in terms of hygiene, health and safety, for example, Muslims can determine to what extent sensual pleasuring of the genitals is permissible.

On the other hand, modern Muslims stumble upon images or read or hear about oral sex and then the curious but law-abiding scramble to make sense of its rulings and etiquettes; instead of having discovered it on their own terms, within their own moral standards and legal parameters. As a result, feelings are mixed: some find it intriguing, others find it objectionable, even as both parties refrain from outlawing it. Little wonder many modern-day *fatwas* on oral sex express a dichotomous position between its moral detestability and its legal permissibility, very much like Dr Qaradawi's position stated above;[53] which is fair enough considering its vile depictions today.

What we find instructive about this observation is how we can remove any ambivalence or uncertainty in our own personal stance on oral sex. It is best done as a couple in mutual consultations, beginning with first erasing all preconceived notions or previously known depictions of oral sex and then allowing the rulings relevant to sexual relationships to form our own unique, couple-specific stance concerning the participation of the mouth in sensually and sexually pleasuring each other. Rulings to be considered are:

a) **Legal sexual partners:** *Al-Mu'minun 23:1...5, 6* makes it is clear that there are no barriers between married couples pertaining to the enjoyment of the pleasures of the sexual organs, except for the circumstances spelt out as *haram* above. Specifically, the use of any other part of the body like the mouth or hands is not included in these prohibitions, with the expressed exception of the anus.

b) **Hygiene standards:** We all know that the sexual organs are located near several openings that discharge impurity or *najasa* from the body. Apart from urine and excrement, which should not be an issue if we comply with Islam's high standards of genital hygiene, there are also other bodily secretions which accompany sexual stimulation like semen and the lubricating liquids. Although the semen *(mani)* is not considered *najis* or impure, when ejaculated, it is often mixed with its lubricating liquid *(madhi)*, which is considered a filth. Likewise, the liquid that lubricates the vaginal wall when a woman is sexually stimulated is similarly regarded as filth. So, all secretions from aroused genitals are either filth or mixed with filth, virtually inseparable after secretion. Hence to swallow, suck, lick or hold these secretions in the mouth is forbidden on account of the general Islamic prohibition against the consumption of filth.

This does not make oral sex forbidden. It is the consumption of filth which is forbidden. A couple can choose together how to avoid the forbidden aspects. It may be difficult, but not impossible if you consider that the male secretions issue from the urethra at the tip of the penis whereas the

SEX, SOUL AND ISLAM

sexually sensitive regions of the male genitalia are much greater than that and do not issue any secretions, ordinarily. As for the female secretions, they do not come from the clitoris which is located near the top of the vulva. The source of the vaginal lubricants are the Bartholin glands which are located further down the vulva near the vaginal opening. If the couple can figure out how to avoid the secretions and are mutually willing parties, oral stimulation of the genitals is legally neutral whether or not it leads all the way to orgasm.

c) Consent and willingness: Legally, sexual refusal and disability are valid grounds for dissolution of a marriage. Even so, this ruling refers strictly to sexual intercourse. It does not apply to other forms of sexual gratification, even if the acts themselves are permitted in Islam. Although marriages have been annulled and divorces granted on grounds of sex deprivation, it has never been over oral sex or any other erotic experimentation with positions, techniques, trends or devices. Instead, any coercion or harassment over these practices can be used against the offender in a judicial process. Above all, any attempts at arousal can only enhance the sexual experience if the participant is willing, which makes it senseless and illegal to impose it on an unwilling spouse, very much for the same reasons we discussed regarding marital rape in Chapter Two.

d) Safety and health: An important principle of Islamic law is the preservation of human life. Hence, any practice which is detrimental to human life, safety and health is forbidden. There are many reports linking oral sex to mouth and throat cancer[54] so be sure to study the evidence and consult medical experts. If there is overwhelming evidence that the practice exposes you to fatal danger or if you are not able to avoid the harmful secretions then you should consider it as forbidden. Otherwise, if you are sure you can avoid the health risks, it is permissible for you.

On the other hand, if for whatever reason, your partner is not willing to take this health risk, his or her unwillingness is enough to disqualify oral sex from your own couple-specific limit of permissibility. Similarly, but on a less dramatic note, oral sex can also increase the possibility of genital infections, even those not usually considered as sexually transmitted disease, like vaginal yeast infections.[55] Although these infections are not potentially fatal like cancer, they can cause considerable discomfort and pain in the nether regions. Therefore, if a spouse is not willing to risk such irritations, the same point applies.

e) Piety does not overrule rulings: It has been argued that the mouth, which is used frequently in reciting the Quran and prayers, should not be in touch with the lowly genitals. However, since there are no specific statements from the Prophet 𐰀 or the Quran concerning this, it cannot be taken as a ruling. After all, other organs like the eyes and hands also participate in the recitation of the Quran and prayers. By the same logic, they too should not be in contact with the genitals which would pretty much confine sex to just intercourse. At best, this can only be taken as a pious concern. If you want to refrain from oral sex on grounds of piety, it is your prerogative, but to give it the same weightage as the other parameters defined by *sharia* when considering its permissibility with your spouse is incorrect.

In summary, the ruling on oral sex may not have been explicitly spelt out by the Quran and the Prophet 𐰀. However, the parameters of permissible sexual behaviour are already clear: spouses are free to explore any means of sexual enjoyment bearing in mind forbidden circumstances, hygiene standards, mutual willingness, safety and health. These parameters should guide couples on how far to go in pleasuring each other with limits which are internally derived to be specific and unique to them as every couple is indeed unique.

In other words, be free to engage in mutual pleasuring with all organs and senses until it reaches the permissible limits. You may be surprised by the levels of pleasure that can be reached. By contrast, experimenting with oral sex for the sake of being up to date with mainstream trends may inadvertently impose values, sensitivities and preferences which are alien to a couple and when the pressure to conform or satisfy a curiosity becomes overwhelming, it leads to tensions and frictions on the relationship, instead of pleasure.

Kinky Sex

Left to human ingenuity and free will, there is no end to sexual innovations. Thankfully, as it gets kinkier, the permissible and the forbidden becomes easier to differentiate, helping us to navigate these sexual acts around our values.

Threesomes: When it comes to threesomes, whether the spouse is involved or not or if the third party is human or otherwise, the very involvement of a third party negates the idea of sexual exclusivity for spouses as defined by *Al-Mu'minun* 23:1...5, 6. For that matter, this prohibition applies in cases involving a husband with two wives in a polygamous marriage because the two wives are not considered spouses. And the same applies with orgies involving more partners, within marriage or otherwise.

Be free to engage in mutual pleasuring with all organs and senses until it reaches the permissible limits. You may be surprised by the levels of pleasure that can be reached.

Foreign objects: Even if a foreign inanimate object is operated by one spouse on the other, this approach still violates the commandment to "guard their private parts except with their spouses". The prohibition ensures that the sexual relationship is maintained exclusively between the two legal partners by excluding the possibility of either or both of them becoming sexually dependant on these devices instead of each other. Truth be told, some of these devices may actually be better than humans functionally. For example, the vibrator is said to be superior to a human in stimulating the clitoris to orgasm,[56] and pleasure dolls now replicate perfect human skin to augment the impossibly perfect bodily proportions and genital functions of a dream virgin girl. In the end though, whether or not the Gigolo Joe depicted in the film *Artificial Intelligence* becomes a reality, the line for Muslim couples has been drawn clearly by the Quran.

In its spirit, the prohibition tells us not to be lazy by taking convenient, even if effective, shortcuts to sexual gratification. Instead, any difficulty, inability or shortcoming in sexual relations should be addressed honestly and sensitively, partner-to-partner or, if need be, with expert professional help; so that the exclusivity of sexual enjoyment is kept between "... mates that you may find tranquillity in them" (*Al-Rum 30:21*). It is important to note that the prohibition goes only as far as it involves the genitals based on the phrase "... guard their private parts ..." The limit for sensual pleasuring between spouses need not be as stringent as intercourse or sexual pleasuring, if it has not been clearly stated by God and His Prophet 🕋. For example, using feathers, flowers, soft fabric, wooden massage balls or even the vibrator on non-genital parts of the body to relieve tired muscles, soothe tense joints, delight the skin, relax the body or destress the mind – be it as an end in itself or as a build up to sexual activities – is all about sensual pleasuring. It should not be confused with sexual pleasuring or intercourse for which this prohibition was introduced.

To most people, if these gadgets and devices are free from human representations, they would ordinarily not invoke imaginations of third-party involvement. However, if the inanimate objects are shaped like a human being (like a full-scale pleasure doll) or human body parts (like dildos or breast pillows) it becomes more complicated. Even if it is confined to sensual pleasuring between consenting spouses, these human representations may have an effect on human imaginations. It is best discussed under the next category.

Imagination and roleplay: Police-and-thief, doctor-and-patient or boss-and-secretary scenarios are examples of sexual roleplay people partake in to spice up their sexual routine. Sometimes, the scenarios they invent may involve themselves in unmarried situations, like when they were courting or interacting with an old-flame or a hot celebrity in place of a spouse, but because the scenarios happen in the mind, it appears that no sin has been committed. Thus, sexual roleplay should be permissible; except that the Prophet 🕊 said, "Allah has forgiven my *ummah* for whatever crosses their mind so long as they do not speak of it or act upon it" (Bukhari).

Out of Allah's mercy, any indecent idea that crosses a person's mind is forgiven by Him because admittedly sometimes ideas come into our imagination beyond our control. However, to speak of or act upon it involves our choice and that makes us responsible for those thoughts from that point onwards. Therefore, planning and discussing any illegal tryst scenario which is basically a *zina* or fornication scene and then acting it out in a roleplay can no longer be considered as beyond our control. Although the bodily act is between two legally married persons, the seat of intention which is the heart, wishes and longs for the *zina* which makes it fall into the definition of "lesser *zina*" as defined by the Prophet 🕊:

> Each son of Adam has his share of fornication (zina). The zina of the eyes is looking, the zina of the ears is listening, the zina of the tongue is speaking, the zina of the hand is touching, and the zina of the foot is walking. The heart wishes and longs and the private part confirms that or denies it.
>
> (Muslim)

Furthermore, what is forbidden in Islam is not just fornication per se, but even approaching it is forbidden, as warned of in the following verse:

> And do not approach unlawful sexual intercourse. Indeed, it is ever an immorality and is evil as a way.
> (Al-Isra 17:32)

This is where both sensual pleasuring with human replicas and certain types of sexual scenarios fall. The likes of pleasure dolls, dildos and breast pillows leave very little to the imagination. In fact, even having these things in the bedroom is as forbidden as having nude sculptures in the living room or pornographic images as bedroom wall decorations. Even though these imitations are not real, they are forbidden in Islam on the basis of *Al-Isra 17:32*. Not only are they not permitted for use by one person, Islam does not condone a threesome involving a pleasure doll, even if no penetration is involved. This is from the legal point of view. Its

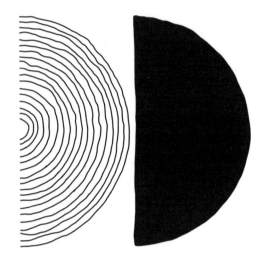

The general **rule** in Islamic jurisprudence is that all things are **permissible** unless otherwise **stated**. However, their permissibility and decency are **not universal** but are rather couple-specific or **situation-centric** in nature.

practical harm to a couple's relationship is identical to that posed by pornography (discussed in Chapter Four).

In summary, sexual roleplay is only permissible if a couple is able to invent scenarios which are free from elements of fornication or any Islamically forbidden encounters. It is important that we maintain our chastity in body and spirit as it is a key element in the sanctity of the marital union.

BDSM – bondage, dominance, sadism, masochism: Apparently, traditional lovemaking is known as "vanilla sex" to some people – nice and sweet, but not quite exciting enough. They desire something beyond the niceties of lovemaking. So, they turn to the thrill of dominating or being dominated, often involving pain and humiliation as well as other experiences which are otherwise viewed in negative terms. They play out extreme scenarios with pre-agreed dominant and submissive roles (dom and sub), sometimes in turns but not necessarily. We see this depicted in films and television programmes with characters clad in uncomfortable leather or metal costumes, with one chained to bedframes or torture themed props, getting whipped or near-suffocated by the other. A popular recent film *Fifty Shades of Grey* is a study of the interpersonal dynamics between such a couple both in everyday life and when engaging in BDSM.

Proponents would point out that a proper BDSM relationship comes with pre-agreed scenarios and rules, complete with delineations of hard limits and soft limits, a signed contract and exit or safety code-words to indicate when a "sub" wants out. This is an attempt to justify that BDSM is not really an abusive relationship and if the couple mutually agrees and abides by these safety rules, it is actually no riskier than rock-climbing or sky-diving which are legally neutral activities if safety can be ensured. But is this the reality?

There is a difference between managing the risks of a thrilling adventure and finding a thrill in the risks themselves. For that matter, even if an adventure sport is legally neutral when safety can be ensured, it becomes forbidden if the participant has become hooked to the risk itself instead of the original activity. For example, managing the risk of fire for hot-air ballooning is definitely not the same as getting a kick through touching the fire. The issue goes beyond the risk of harm, but the mentality behind taking those risks. The Islamic perspective is based on the hadith, "No harm may be inflicted on oneself or others" (Muwatta). It is not the harm which is forbidden, but the intention to cause pain or humiliation. In other words, whether or not there is any physical harm done, a Muslim cannot inflict that intention on themselves or on others.[57] Since by definition, BDSM seeks the thrill in the bondage and domination of a partner (sadism) or the self (masochism); with harm, pain, injury and humiliation being par for the course, it is forbidden.

However, we must also consider that BDSM is a huge umbrella term ranging from an extreme like the sexual torture chamber scenario to the relatively innocuous act of tying up and blindfolding a spouse with shiny silk scarves for one-way sexual pleasuring. What makes both examples of BDSM is the element of power play. In the latter scenario, the voluntary loss of control without the element of pain and humiliation, produces a liberating arousal in the "sub" as the conjugal duty to satisfy is lifted and the "sub" is left with nothing to do except enjoy the experience. In such a case, it is not forbidden. Some may contend this is pseudo-BDSM, but not its proponents as they defend it against accusations of abuse, like Diva Toolbox who said, "if all you're doing is ... being blindfolded with a silk scarf, that can be called BDSM."[58]

We shall end here as BDSM is adequately representative of the difficulty in determining the Islamic rulings on some of the more complicated sexual behaviours of our times. The rulings can no longer be one-size-fits-all. So, if you want to keep up with what others are doing sexually, you will have to pick and choose to suit your values or allow their values to dominate your life. The alternative is to avoid them completely. Either way, do not expect a clear-cut religious opinion *(fatwa)* or ruling *(hukum)* on these issues.

There is wisdom in this. We do not advocate that multiple sources of knowledge on enriching your sex life should be applied in their entirety. Our advice is to learn from others, enrich your ideas and expand your vocabulary of pleasuring. In order to do this in an Islamically sanctioned way, the believer must separate the act itself from the intentions and values behind it. If the concept is in keeping with Islamic values you may practise them after improving the objectionable aspects of their execution.

A moral rule of thumb for sexual adventurism is that it should be an extension of mutual pleasuring, in its true sense – truly mutual and truly pleasurable; and not about the maximisation of sexual gratification for its own sake, because the latter end-goal can be alienating instead of enhancing relationships. After which, the legal requirements must be met, namely avoidance of the *haram* circumstances and compliance to Islamic standards of hygiene, consent and welfare.

Conclusion

The current generation of marriageable Muslim youths is more exposed than ever to explicit mainstream depictions of certain sexual behaviours they are not already familiar with. It is important to illustrate how such behaviours are to be viewed from an Islamic perspective. This gives Muslim couples the opportunity to explore together in a way which does not compromise Islamic values. The overriding goal of any sexual activity should be the attainment of mutual pleasure and bliss as husband and wife honour the exclusive privilege granted them by Allah ﷻ. The guidelines afforded to us by the Quran and Sunna are the perfect framework within which to pursue this aim. Of course, Allah ﷻ knows best.

Society's overall progress in sexual knowledge and skills had not necessarily translated into sexual satisfaction for both genders.

SHERE HITE

Chapter 4
The Sexual Experience

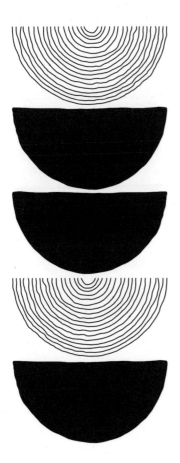

Introduction: The Meaning of *Akhlaq*

Verily, I have been sent to complete the respectable disposition (of mankind).

(Bukhari)

The word "disposition" above is translated from the Arabic word *akhlaq* and the hadith explains the ultimate objective of the Prophet Muhammad's 🕌 teachings. Islam is founded on an understanding of the purpose of life as we discover it in Islam's belief system and moves on to provide implementable injunctions in manifesting these beliefs into action. The Prophet's 🕌 statement above means that beyond putting beliefs into action, his ultimate objective is the embodiment of these beliefs in the very personality of the believer.

Significantly, the attainment of an Islamic personality requires more than the acquirement of knowledge or the performance of deeds but necessarily involves a process of cultivation and nurturing. Hence, an Islamic teacher also plays the role of a cultivator (*murabbi*) of character. Very much like a farmer who observes, nourishes and even prunes his growing crop, a *murabbi* develops by monitoring, teaching, advising and admonishing to cultivate the character of his students.

However, nurturing is not confined to formal teacher-student settings only. For example, parents too hold the role of *murabbis* with regards to their children. Likewise, couples are expected to be mutual nurturers to one another. Even if husband and wife are far from perfect in character, knowledge and skills, what is more important is the commitment to a lifetime of care, support and devotion to one another in the common pursuit of that perfection. With that in mind, this chapter is about preparing for a lifetime of mutual nurturing, namely in the attainment of the Quranic ideal:

And of His signs is that He created for you from yourselves mates that you may find tranquillity in them; and He placed between you love and mercy. Indeed in that are signs for a people who give thought.
(Al-Rum 30:21)

As discussed in Chapter Two, good sex cannot be forced nor legislated but must be nurtured and cultivated like all other aspects of human relationships. For that, couples need to go beyond the legality of sex towards the refinement of its experience. Too much of the Islamic literature and discourse today is centred around the categorisations of *halal* and *haram*, but ultimately the development of positive relationships requires more than the clinical observance of rules and etiquettes. Whether it is God-consciousness through prayer, self-restraint through fasting or community-spiritedness through *zakat*, moral prescriptions provide an important starting point. However, the development of our values and character depend on the on-going process of monitoring, sustaining, and enhancing these traits in our daily lives (*tarbiya*) as well as cleansing ourselves of the contradictory values that may unintentionally develop within us (*tazkiya*).

Likewise, verse *Al-Rum 30:21* does not guarantee that "mating" will automatically result in tranquillity, love and mercy. In order to grow and blossom in a marriage, they require the same nurturing and pruning process and like with any other *amal* (good deed), the cultivation of these values requires us to be familiar with the inner workings of that *amal* itself – in this case, sex – its effects on human relationships and the common issues surrounding its practice. We need to keep learning and relearning about sex as we explore it in early marriage, keep the flame of mutual desire burning throughout, discover its new dimensions in old age and instil positive sexual values in our growing children.

In this chapter, we will endeavour to cover all the areas which will assist couples on their journey of growth and discovery. We begin with the basic similarities and differences between the male and female sexual experience. That will allow us to understand the Prophet's 🌸 insights on sex which helps to reduce the gender-gap of sexual perception. Then we will discuss how this prophetic outlook towards sex can be sustained throughout marriage, from the first night to the busiest days of mid-marriage, right through to the meno and andropausal period. Finally, we will address some common sexual myths we encounter in counselling.

Understanding the Sexual Experience

There may be those of us who object to learning about the details of sex for fear it will take away from its mystery and excitement. The truth is, no amount of knowledge will do that. In fact, understanding sex will only enhance the experience of it. By remaining sexually ignorant, couples may find the secrets and intricacies of sex to be confusing or intimidating, whereas for those who seek knowledge, its mysteries are alluring and exciting, something to be explored and enjoyed. Knowledge is empowering and there are so many layers of the sexual experience to be discovered. We will begin by looking at modern scientific findings.

The Physiological Experience

The human sexual response cycle was explained by Johnson and Masters in their ground-breaking 1966 publication *Human Sexual Response.*[59] The term "sexual response" refers to the natural urge in adult animals to mate and reproduce. It also exists in the human body which is animalistic in nature. However, unlike animals, mankind is also given intellect and choice. So, whether the human sexual response remains supressed or becomes wild is within the control of the human being. The term "cycle" refers to a process that follows a specific sequence. The "life-cycle of a mosquito" for example goes through the stages of egg, larvae, pupa, adult, egg again and so on. Every stage depends on the one before. In the same sense, the "human sexual response cycle" is a scientific model to explain what a human being experiences in a complete and satisfying sexual activity. The cycle consists of four phases known as excitement, plateau, orgasm and resolution.

Excitement initiates the cycle when the person is stimulated, be it physically, mentally or both. This may be achieved through caresses, kisses, fondling, fragrance, erotic whispers, seeing a beautiful body or through the power of the imagination. The list is limitless. The most obvious indication of excitement is penile erection and lubrication of the vaginal walls – two basic bodily changes which are crucial for copulation to be pleasurable.

Plateau refers to the phase when the excitement is enhanced and then sustained and maintained for the sake of savouring its pleasures, instead of letting it reach its climax. The phase can be prolonged or shortened depending on the person's skill in balancing the rise and fall of the erotic wave while keeping it just below a certain "point of no return". It is very much like someone savouring their favourite food, keeping it on their tongue and palette to let its flavours linger, instead of hastily swallowing.

Orgasm happens when the intensity of erotic pleasure, whether deliberately or otherwise, is raised above a certain threshold where the rise and fall can no longer be controlled by the person. At this point, the pleasure takes on a life of its own, hijacking the mind and body both in a dizzying crescendo. Though the orgasm itself is fleeting, its feel-good effect lingers for as long as memory serves. The orgasm's epicentre is near the genital regions, but it lashes out wavelike towards every part of the human body, mind and soul. Normally, it is accompanied by ejaculation of semen and vaginal contractions – two bodily responses that aid insemination.

Resolution is the last phase of the cycle. Here, mind and body feel a deep relaxation, so deep that some are sent to sleep in this phase. The raging urges are pacified as the body travels through this phase back to its pre-excitement state until new forms of stimulation initiate a new cycle.

Both men and women go through the same cycle in identical order. However, although the cycle is naturally sequenced, it is not automatic. In other words, excitement does not guarantee orgasm but instead requires on-going and sustained

SEX, SOUL AND ISLAM

stimulation and it can be stunted and even reversed if the stimulation ceases or external disturbances like pain, noise or distraction in thoughts occur. Whether the cycle is completed depends more on the quality of stimulation than intercourse. For example, a good head-to-toe sensual massage with no intercourse can bring about a complete cycle including orgasm for both men and women in the hands of a skilful partner. On the other hand, an intercourse forced upon an insufficiently aroused or worse still, unwilling spouse will not bring about excitement, let alone orgasm. Such intercourse is not only unsatisfactory; it is at best irritating and at worst physically and psychologically injurious. Therefore, in a satisfactory sexual experience, the human sexual response cycle runs smoothly and completely. It is the same for both genders in that sense. However, there are differences between male and female.

By and large, a man's sexual arousal is easier to ignite than a woman's. For example, the mere sight of the female physique is enough to stimulate his excitement, let alone her touch, scent and voice. The average man can go from excitement to orgasm in five minutes. Due to this ease and speed, men have difficulty in maintaining the plateau phase, resulting in unintended orgasm. When resolution takes place, the penis deflates and the entire body slumbers even as he is still "needed" by his wife.

On the other hand, women's arousal is slower and not so easy to instigate. On average and with good stimulation, a woman's cycle needs fifteen minutes to reach orgasm. This slow build-up is a gift that facilitates women in savouring the exquisite pleasures of the plateau phase. Furthermore, unlike men, a woman need not fall completely into the resolution phase but can arouse another cycle almost immediately after an orgasm, thereby triggering multiple orgasms, depending on her choice and physical stamina. This is not to suggest that she does not experience the resolution phase after orgasm, but that it affects her differently.

Findings like this have increased sexual knowledge among the masses and popularised sexual stimulation techniques, especially the concept of "foreplay".

> In recent years the importance of foreplay to sexual enjoyment has been widely acknowledged ... Since it takes longer for women to be vaginally lubricated sufficiently for intercourse than it does for men to achieve erection and be ready (Masters and Johnson 1966), perhaps this acknowledgement represents an increased understanding of women's needs to be sexually stimulated for a longer period of time than men prior to coitus.
>
> (Jerrold Greenberg et al.)[60]

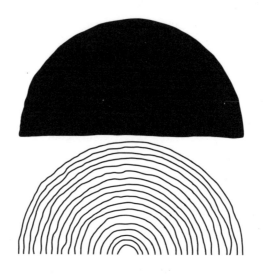

Good sex cannot be **forced** nor **legislated** but must be **nurtured** and cultivated like all other aspects of human **relationships**. For that, couples need to go **beyond** the legality of sex towards the **refinement** of its experience.

Yet, by 1976 Shere Hite was documenting women's wide-spread sexual dissatisfaction, despite an increase among men in sexual knowledge and skills. Apparently, women felt "... men are not exactly uninformed; they seem to know about all the right places of a woman's body, but too often most of them seem to be just not tuned into Woman", and "... the more confident they are of their sexual prowess and the effectiveness of their technique, the more ignorant they seem to be of the facts and realities". Her book *The Hite Report: A Nationwide Study of Female Sexuality* argued that society's overall progress in sexual knowledge and skills had not necessarily translated into sexual satisfaction for both genders.[61]

The Psycho-Emotional Factor Called Desire

In the late 1970s, other therapists and researchers began to look beyond physiology to understand the sexual experience. Among others, in 1979, Helen Kaplan introduced "desire" – a psycho-emotional state of readiness or willingness for sex – into the equation when she developed a tri-phasic model comprising of "desire, excitement and resolution".[62] Kaplan's model does not contradict Johnson and Masters' mainly physiological sexual response cycle nor is it a mere addition to its phases as "desire" is intricately involved in its smooth-running and completion in no particular order or sequence.

Perhaps, the easiest way to understand desire's link to sex is to compare it with the appetite's link to eating. Obviously, if a dish tastes bad, it will spoil your appetite, but there are times when no matter how delicious you know a dish is, if you have no appetite, you can't even bear to taste, let alone enjoy it. Often, you can lose your appetite not because of the food per se, but other external factors like the way the food looks, the cleanliness, noisiness or smell of the surroundings you are eating in or your personal state of wellness. Likewise, sexual desire is dependent on many factors external to sex such as the attractive personality of a partner, a romantic setting, a peaceful environment as well as a healthy day-to-day relationship between husband and wife. These are the things that determine if a person wants to be with another. Sexual desire starts with this basic willingness, or better still, yearning for another person's company and that is a psycho-emotional phenomenon.

Even though desire is crucial, adequate physical stimulation is still required to arouse, enhance and complete the physiological cycle. Just as a good appetite which encourages eating disappears if the food does not taste good, desire will cease without stimulation. Saying that, there are cases where physical titillation can trigger desire, very much like a tasty, well-presented dish can make a fussy eater want to eat. There are also those who can overcome their lack of appetite to eat for the sake of survival and health.

Through their research, Kaplan and her contemporaries[63] were able to distinguish desire-related sexual dysfunctions from physiology-related problems which further improved sexual understanding. Ever since, the focus in sexual discourse has turned towards more subjective psycho-emotional factors. By the turn of the century, the role of desire had occupied pole position. In his 2006 book *He Comes Next*, sex-therapist Dr Ian Kerner describes the key difference between male and female sexual experience as such:

> *For men, desire and arousal are virtually one and the same. Give a*
> *guy a hard-on and he wants to use it. But for women, desire usually*
> *requires components that don't necessarily need to be present for men:*
> *intimacy, affection, trust, humour, respect and security among others.*
> *Men appreciate those qualities, but we don't necessarily need them*
> *to get turned on and have sex. This difference in how men experience*
> *desire explains why men are more easily able to compartmentalize*
> *between sex and love.*
>
> (Ian Kerner)[64]

So, even though a neat, all-encompassing sexual theory is yet to be developed, this insight into desire gives us a decent working understanding of the sexual experience. At least we know that both men and women experience sex in the physiological and psycho-emotional sense. The physiological aspect of sex proceeds in a specific order from excitement to plateau, on to the orgasm and resolution phases, in a satisfactory experience, but whether or not the physiological cycle can be initiated, sustained, enhanced, fulfilled, terminated or reversed depends on the psycho-emotional state called desire. And Kerner has identified a key distinction between male and female desire.

For a man, desire-arousal is a two-way street. Desire naturally leads to arousal, but even when it is absent, physiologically stimulated arousal can bring it on. In a woman though, it is a one-way street. Desire invites arousal, but if desire is absent, even the most skilful lover cannot invoke female arousal, let alone desire itself. That cliché of a man busy working on his laptop being easily seduced by his wife "accidentally" dropping her towel as she exits the shower is not far from the truth. A wispy caress here, a gentle fondle there will usually seal the deal. Such a distraction is very likely regarded by most men as welcome relief or even a source of inspiration, but try doing that to a busy woman. A man exposing his private parts or worse still, her private parts when uninvited is not appealing to a woman. At best, these attempts at seducing her will serve as funny memories to laugh over, if their

SEX, SOUL AND ISLAM

general relationship is healthy to start with, but if they become habit, most women will regard them as a manifestation of a husband's insensitivity to her needs and wants. If a man persists in such behaviour, even when it is not welcomed, it is very likely a signifier of wider problems in the marriage.

Of course, all norms have exceptions, including this arousal-desire connection in men. In counselling, we have come across cases of husbands completely losing their desire despite their wives' physical stimulations and undisputable evidence that their arousal-desire connection was working fine under other circumstances. We will discuss this later while discussing the common myth that men will always be able to perform. But for the vast majority of men, in normal, healthy relationships, desire invites arousal and vice-versa. However, it is a little more complex in women.

The Elusive Female Desire

Female desire is mysterious and elusive to men and women alike. It is not something that only clueless husbands should be blamed for because even wives sometimes don't understand why they're not in the mood for sex. In fairy tales, the hero always wins the girl in the predictable format of seduction: presenting her with flowers, using sweet words or just good looks, singing love songs under her balcony and of course, slaying the fire-breathing dragons. In real life however, husbands and wives alike are finding that female desire does not follow any particular script. For example, not all women love flowers. Women growing up poor, living from hand to mouth, for example, may even see them as a waste of money. Even those who appreciated such gifts during courtship or early marriage may not do so in mid-marriage as the bills, mortgage and putting food on the table puts strain on a couple's joint-income. Likewise, a love song, even when sung by a guitar-plucking baritone, is hardly romantic to a wife left alone to prepare dinner or clean the house after her own long day at the office. In such cases, a helping hand would be much more appreciated. As for rescuing damsels in distress, many women nowadays would rather fight their own battles and find unsolicited chivalry off-putting.

When it comes to female desire, there are no fixed formulas and what worked in the past may not work today. What she loves today she may hate tomorrow. Times change, things change, even she changes. Yet some men still cling to their old pick-up lines and clichéd ideas throughout marriage, and when these do not work, they always have the elusive female desire to blame.

Then there are those men who in the case of their wife, believe that since they already "got the girl", they can bypass the other phases of seduction and begin directly with genital stimulation; also with the "tried and tested" techniques and knowledge of erotic hot-spots gleaned from men's magazines, porn and other pop-culture portrayals of the sexual process. Such men may discover for themselves what Shere Hite had documented in 1976, where even polished sexual techniques do not result in a woman's arousal and can in fact turn her off: "I resent men engaging in some activity because they think it will stimulate me. I doubt that clitoral stimulation is even remotely interesting to men except that it makes them feel powerful in getting a reaction from the woman. I do not cooperate with patronising nonsense."[65]

In the heyday of the sexual revolution, women were open to sex and men were well educated in sexual knowledge and had plenty of practice to hone their skills and techniques. So, men went to bed confident in giving willing women a rolling good time, not realising that although foreplay manoeuvres never failed to fire men on towards orgasm, it was not necessarily the case with women, as expressed by one woman, "Yes I feel anxiety, distrust and resentment at being manoeuvred, even in disguised forms; I don't like feeling I'm being 'worked on' by someone who feels I should have orgasms".[66]

In Hite's study, women from across the US express their revulsion to men's sexual hubris. Of course, this does not mean that American women in the 1970s were the first to feel this way. It was the first time a woman had bravely documented women's sexual frustrations and published it world-wide,[67] but who knows how many women throughout human history have lamented the lack of understanding of their sexual needs on the part of men. Unfortunately, this problem is still ongoing.

We have come across cases of wives feeling irritated by the mechanical stimulations of husbands oblivious to their preferences, ideas and at times, protestations. To them it feels more like being prepared for penetration instead of being genuinely desired by their spouse, but many in our community do not have the wherewithal to give and receive feedback on each other's feelings during sex. Under such circumstances, women's reactions vary from avoiding sex with a thousand excuses to finding secret lovers, learning to fake it or suffering the intrusions in the name of wifely duty. Their predicament is not far from one Hite Report entry, which is very telling about what really turns women off men: "Men are not exactly uninformed; they seem to know about all the right places of a woman's body, but too often **most of them seem to be just not tuned into Woman**".[68]

In our sex enrichment workshops, among long-married couples, we have an exercise asking groups of men and women separately to suggest activities that will turn each other on. As would be expected, every suggestion raises mixed reactions but that is fine because it is more of a brainstorming than a consensus building exercise. One type of suggestion though, will always receive unanimous enthusiastic agreement among female participants; namely husbands sharing the burden of household chores, such as, "doing the laundry", "putting the children to bed" or even, "bathing elderly or sick parents".

While women are always excited over these ideas, the participating men generally see such suggestions as clever tricks to obtain their labour. Indeed, at first glance these menial tasks have nothing to do with desire, love, romance, intimacy and least of all, sex, but not if we consider them from the viewpoint of a typical wife's daily burdens, where she is still expected to run the household even when she too works full-time to supplement her husband's income. In view of these daily struggles, these ideas express to the wife that her husband is understanding of and empathetic towards her condition and needs.

That is why, for most women in mid-marriage, cleaning the toilet makes a man far more desirable than an expensive bouquet of flowers. These are the acts that genuinely show the man is "tuned into (his) woman" and that is what women desire in men more than anything else. It is no coincidence that the Prophet ﷺ was self-sufficient regarding his personal needs, non-critical of the way his wives carried out their household duties and helpful around the home, "The Messenger of Allah ﷺ however, used to sew his own clothes, mend his own shoes and do whatever other workmen do in their homes," and "He was like any other human being: he would clean his clothes, milk his ewe and serve himself" (Ahmad). In a hadith reported by Muslim, Jabir relates that the Holy Prophet ﷺ once asked his household members for curry. They told him that there was nothing but vinegar. He called for it and started eating his food with it, exclaiming, "The best curry is vinegar; the best curry is vinegar" and in a narration reported by Bukhari, Aisha ﷺ said, "The Prophet ﷺ used to remain busy serving and helping the inmates of his house, and when the time for prayer would come, he would go out for the same."

In the same vein, author Kathy Lette describes what makes international heart-throb, George Clooney, so attractive, "I must say, if you want to know why George Clooney is the ultimate love god, after dinner he cleared the table and stacked the dishwasher. That is foreplay for females."[69] However, we should not confuse the form for its substance. The key to attraction is not just the act of a man doing the housework, but what it represents. Other similar turn-ons may be a husband's support of his wife's career advancement, hobbies or even her favourite sports team. In essence, what stokes a woman's desire for a man is his pure, sincere, unselfish desire for her in the truest sense of the word – her feelings, thoughts, aspirations, needs and values. This is not confined to her psycho-emotional needs only but also include awareness of her sexual moods. So, to be blunt, if what she craves for in that moment is hot penetrative sex but instead, he fusses her with his sweet little concern over her grandmother's in-grown toe-nail, that is equally a turn-off.

In other words, the secret to female desire is not in some idea, object or technique which can be copied or repeated blindly. Nor does it need to be, because the secret is actually her! The female desire is unleashed by the male's pure, untainted desire for her as manifested in the interest, sensitivity and empathy he shows her. This is only elusive to the man who cannot see beyond his needs, as one of the women from Shere Hite explains, "The unique men are those who have outgrown the need for techniques, etc, and are comfortable offering themselves. The important thing is just to listen to yourself and to the other person."[70]

Understanding the Sunna on Lovemaking

Through the exploration of modern scientific sexual knowledge, we do not mean to suggest it was modern Western science that first opened the doors to sexual understanding. We started from that vantage point only because Muslims today are more likely to understand explanations deriving from empirically researched viewpoints, but we should also be open to the knowledge contained in proverbs, songs, customs, ancient sex manuals and even the romantic fairy tales we mentioned earlier, because despite their unrealistic and misleading portrayals of romance, they still contain lessons regarding love, intimacy and sexual enjoyment if we can sift the wheat from the chaff. More importantly, there is no reason to doubt that ancient wisdom too addresses sexual ignorance, chauvinism and exploitation, all of which have plagued mankind throughout history.

In the Islamic traditions, we have Saidina Ali ﷺ, the Prophet's ﷺ close companion and son-in-law, alluding to the irony of the way males and females experience sexual desire, centuries before *Human Sexual Response* was published, "Almighty Allah ﷻ created sexual desires in ten parts; then He gave nine parts to women and one to men. (But then Allah ﷻ) also gave them equal parts of shyness" (Sayyid Muhammad Rizvi).[71] In other words, nine parts of shyness are given to women and one part to men. Only the wise would know of women's true prowess behind their veils of shyness, modesty and respectability as opposed to men's sexual forthrightness which belies their lesser capacity.

As it is not part of Islamic tradition to question the logic of God-created mismatches but instead to seek the wisdom behind them, Muslim sages over the years have always recognised that it takes wisdom to be mesmerised by the splendour of women whereas ignorance will lead to their subjugation and oppression. The following words were attributed to the twelfth century Muslim mystic and poet, Jalal ad-Din Muhammad Rumi, "... women totally dominate men of intellect and possessors of hearts, but ignorant men dominate women, for they are shackled by

SEX, SOUL AND ISLAM

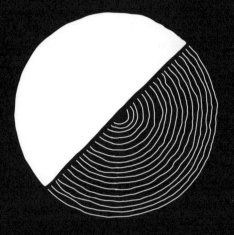

By remaining sexually **ignorant**, couples may find the secrets and **intricacies** of sex to be **confusing** or intimidating, whereas for those who **seek** knowledge, its mysteries are alluring and **exciting.**

the ferocity of animals."[72] The physiology of sex here is seen like a "shackle" that limits its full potential. As with food or the beauty of nature, the pleasures of sex are to be savoured but not for their own sake. They are a window from which we can glimpse the infinite pleasures of the Hereafter. In the words of another Muslim sage, Imam Ghazali ﷺ, "The pleasure that is felt in sexual intercourse between a man and his wife is a little sign of the next worldly pleasure ... the greed for pleasure and happiness of Paradise lead a man towards guidance."[73]

Of course, these views are reflections on the examples of the Prophet ﷺ regarding sexual matters. It was part and parcel of the Prophet's ﷺ mission to unshackle us from the animality of sex through practical, implementable guidance for the masses to follow. He did so by introducing the concept of a sexual messenger or go-between that would shepherd the animal towards the spiritual dimensions of sex as well as bringing the male and female experiences of sex closer to each other.

A Messenger Between the Two

In Chapter Two, we discussed several sex-related hadiths which fit into two groups: one directed at men and the other, women. They each address the potential ignorance, neglect and insensitivities of one gender towards the other's sexual particularities. However, there are commonalities between the two genders when it comes to sex. Hence, there is a third hadith which draws both genders towards what they can experience in common. This common experience also distinguishes human lovemaking from animal mating and without such reminders, humans would tend towards the practical, mechanical, perfunctory, even obligatory performance of sex; purely because it is more convenient. That is why the Prophet ﷺ said,

> Let none of you fall suddenly upon his wife like an animal. Let there be
> a messenger between the two. And when someone asked: "What is the
> messenger, O Prophet?" He said: "Kissing and words of love".

> (Dailami)

In many Islamic books, the concept of "messenger" has been translated and explained as the modern concept of "foreplay". We believe this is semantically and conceptually wrong. The word "foreplay" precisely refers to a stage or process that precedes the main performance which in this case refers to penetrative sex, but if that is what the Prophet ﷺ meant, would he not have used words like "precede", "prior" or "initiate" in reference to "the messenger" as a preamble before a husband "fall suddenly upon his wife"? Instead, he asked for

SEX, SOUL AND ISLAM

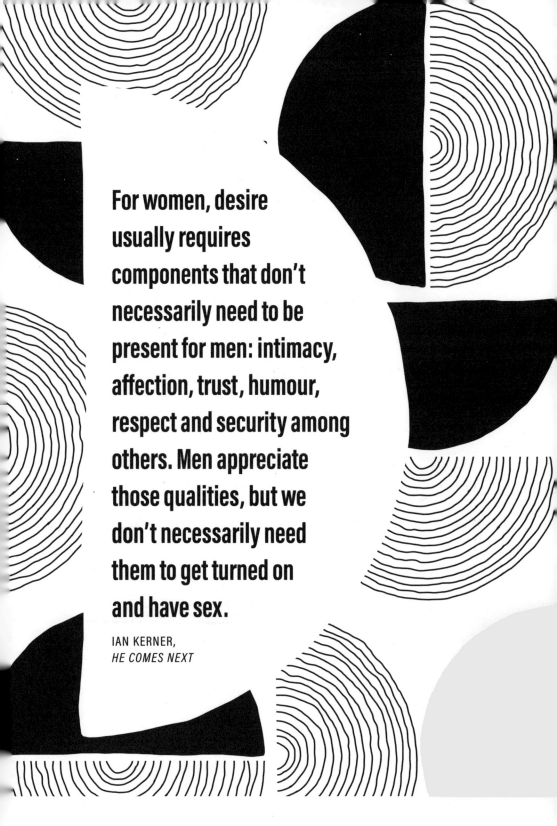

For women, desire usually requires components that don't necessarily need to be present for men: intimacy, affection, trust, humour, respect and security among others. Men appreciate those qualities, but we don't necessarily need them to get turned on and have sex.

IAN KERNER,
HE COMES NEXT

the "messenger" to be "between the two" i.e. between husband and wife, not between intercourse and prior activities, as "foreplay" implies. It is also extremely significant that of all the words in the world, the Prophet ﷺ used "messenger" (*rasul*) for this notion. In Islamic parlance, a *rasul* is not a mere delivery boy or mouthpiece of a message. Instead, a *rasul* guides by living that message day in, day out, making it part and parcel of their way of life. Likewise, this "messenger" is to remain "between the two" before, during and after intercourse.

By the way, "foreplay" is very difficult to translate accurately in many languages because it is a relatively modern concept. In fact, the English word made its dictionary debut in the sexual context only in 1929 having borrowed from theatre the idea of a warm-up gig before the main play.[74] There is no way of telling whether the word is the progenitor or merely an accurate reflection of the then prevalent understanding about sex. Despite the fact that the concept of "foreplay" is now firmly entrenched in the modern understanding of sex, many sexual therapists take issue with the term.

In his book *Sexual Solutions – A Guide for Men and the Women Who Love Them*, Michael Castleman warns, "A widely held notion about lovemaking is that it is divided into three distinct stages: foreplay, intercourse, and afterglow. The very word "foreplay" suggests that it happens before the "real thing." However, the idea that foreplay precedes actually "doing it" is an indirect cause of many men's sexual difficulties."[75]

In *He Comes Next – The Thinking Woman's Guide to Pleasuring a Man* Ian Kerner asserts: With its emphasis on sexual "readiness", foreplay, as defined and practiced, focuses more on stimulating physical arousal than sparking desire ... As a result, we often struggle to create desire from physical arousal. We pop pills and conjure pornographic images to speed the desired effect ... cajoling the brain to follow the body, when it should be the other way around.[76]

In any case, as far as the hadith is concerned, there is no compartmentalisation of sex into appetiser, main course and dessert. There is instead a distinction between animal and human sex. Granted, modern research has shown that certain animal species exhibit sexual habits which are not purely practical. For example, some animal species mate for life although it is counter-productive to procreation. However, when the Prophet ﷺ described practical, mechanical or perfunctory sex as animal-like, he did not rule out the existence of these spectacularly exceptional species. He merely used the sexual habits of most other animals to paint a negative image of perfunctory sex, followed by his advice that we discover the human dimension of lovemaking by first establishing a genuine and complete human-to-human intimacy between man and wife through a "messenger between the two".

Kissing

Men tend to miss the forest for the trees when they become obsessed with their wife's body parts over her as a total person, but couples too suffer from this delusion when they develop a habit of intimacy which is confined to pure genital intercourse, having never experienced the intimacy of two people in all of their totality, encompassing all the senses, emotions and thoughts that make us human.

The hadith we have been discussing means to free us from the carnality of purely genital intercourse so we may discover the pleasures of the five senses, beginning with kissing. In order to truly appreciate the role of the kiss in elevating us to new heights of sensual pleasure and sexual intimacy with our spouse, we must immerse ourselves in it completely, not confining ourselves to the usual understanding of the meeting of lips but instead, allowing the lips to explore the body they have been yearning for. As the lover explores with their mouth, their eyes feast on the contours and curves of the human body, their nose relishes the familiar odour of their spouse, perfumed or otherwise, as it breathes close to wherever the lips go, and their ears take their fill of the groans, moans and sighs emanating from the mouth of their beloved. The more adventurous may let their tongue register the unique tastes their lover's body exudes (although Muslims have precautionary rulings as discussed in Chapter Three), but the greatest potential for pleasure can be found within the body's largest organ – the skin. During a passionate kiss, the hands naturally roam the body, to pleasure and be pleasured by the smooth, soft, hard, warm, moist, curved, sunken and raised features of the lover's skin.

Therefore, it is reasonable to assume that the "kissing" in the hadith does not refer to the perfunctory kiss we give each other as a way of saying "hello" or "goodbye". Nor is it a preparatory procedure for sex, whether or not the kiss is followed by well-studied, well-practiced, full-bodied stimulations. Instead, it refers to the mutual pleasuring of the lovers' senses of sight, smell, hearing, taste and touch as an activity in its own right. It may come before, during or after intercourse or it may have nothing to do with intercourse at all, because there is more to the human body than the genitals; hence there is more to bodily pleasures than intercourse. In fact, intercourse often short-circuits the full spectrum of these physical sensual pleasures from fully maturing as the sexual response cycle hijacks the human body, hurrying it along towards climax. This deprives the couple of even knowing what they are missing.

Another advantage of exploring the sensual pleasures outside intercourse is that they are within human control. They allow us to feel, enjoy, savour and share with a sense of giving and taking of such pleasures in the form of gifts to each other. By indulging in these sensual activities, the couple become more aware of and able to control their own bodily pleasures as well as each other's. So much so, that even when genitals are involved and even in the case of full intercourse, the plateaus and peaks of the sexual response cycle can also be controlled.

If sensual pleasuring is to exist "between the two", regardless of sexual intercourse, it should also exist beyond the bedroom, albeit within limits of decency. This is achievable if couples use those decent, non-sexual gestures to express concern, longing, hope, camaraderie or simply to provide relief. These are gestures that may not necessarily trigger sexual responses, but this makes their power to touch the heart even more potent, precisely because of their innocence. It may take the form of holding hands, slinging an arm over the shoulder or stretching it across the waist during a walk as an outward display of intimacy and affection. We may pat, stroke or squeeze each other's hands, arms or face during conversations as a way of registering our empathy or understanding. Maybe you enjoy talking nonsense with your partner, singing karaoke terribly or just laughing together, all because you find comfort in each other's voices. And at times all we need is to see that familiar smile to re-energise our tired minds after a long day.

Such simple gestures may seem like the obvious activities that married couples engage in without thinking about, but these are in fact the first things to disappear from daily interactions when a relationship stops functioning healthily. This leads to couples placing too much hope on sex to rescue their dry, emotionless day-to-day interplay, never realising that it actually works the other way round. Without those heartfelt, sensuous day-to-day exchanges, it is the sex that will be dry and emotionless; and before long it will become a chore to be endured rather than an experience to be cherished.

Words of Love

The original Arabic text of the hadith only defined "the messenger" as "kissing and words". You will find many books and websites translating the word "*kalam*" into "words of love", no doubt to fit it within the presumed concept of foreplay, but just as with "kissing", "words of love" must be understood as a reference to wider aspects of intimacy which should exist between man and wife within and beyond intercourse. If "kissing" is about bodily senses bringing hearts closer, this is about the meeting of minds through words and words are uniquely human. Be it verbal, written or signed, language allows us to express complex, delicate and sensitive thoughts, wishes and feelings about and to each other. Taken together with the wider meaning of "kissing", this unique human capacity elevates sex beyond its functional role of procreation to become an arena for play, expression and bonding with our lover.

SEX, SOUL AND ISLAM

Perhaps a simple way to understand the role of words in lovemaking is to compare its role to any team sport, for example, football. For players, the draw of the sport goes beyond the game and is more about the socialising that accompanies it. The ball is only an excuse. During play, the team shares banter and encouragement, warns each other of danger and improvises counter-attacks together, they fine tune their techniques and hone their skills through constant communication, they celebrate their goals and share their disappointments, all in solidarity with one another. When the game finishes, they regroup to dissect it, moment by moment, at the same time strategising for future matches. Although the game has ended, the reminiscing may go on for months, or even years after. It happens among amateurs and professionals alike, and all because true football lovers don't just play ball, they talk about it for as long as they are in love with it.

Likewise, there should be lots of talk during lovemaking too. We mentioned the sweet nothings, groans and moans. These may be linguistically meaningless, but they verbalise the deep pleasures of the senses which are otherwise mute and expressionless. Hence, such sounds help to communicate and make feelings understood. Besides these, there are also deliberate cues and feedback that seasoned lovers whisper to each other to express what they want, what they do not want or how their pleasure can be enhanced. These may include directions and encouragements like, "a little to the right darling", "higher", "softer", "wait" or even, "keep going". You may be surprised that such explicit communication takes place during lovemaking, but it is a hallmark of a healthy sexual relationship.

This is because it signifies that husband and wife feel comfortable enough to let each other know what they are thinking and feeling without the fear of being criticised, belittled or unappreciated. When couples reach this level of comfort; they can venture into the most intimate and sensitive topics of sex with the same sense of security. In such instances, discussions around sex are not confined to the bedroom and they become a valuable tool for reviewing what both partners like and don't like, clarifying intentions behind gestures and advances as well as requesting, suggesting or brainstorming new ideas to spice up their future encounters. In short, "words of love" is an advantage humans have over God's other creations, allowing them to communicate, clarify and come to a mutual understanding over intangible concepts, values, meanings, feelings and other matters of the heart which we try to express in our day-to-day sensuous interaction – in and out of bed.

"Kissing" and "words of love" work together as "the messenger". In modern scientific parlance, they refer to the sensual and social aspects of intimacy which should flourish "between the two" every moment of their life, regardless of intercourse. In common terms, romance, banter, frolicking, touchy-feely moments and

The **secret** to female **desire** is **not** in some idea, object or technique which can be **copied** or repeated **blindly**. Nor does it need to be, because the secret is actually **her!**

flirting. Even shared activities, like hobbies and sports should permeate our intimate moments, rather than just the preoccupation with procreation. As the Prophet ﷺ makes clear, the intimate relationship between husband and wife is about more than just procreation and should include fun and play:

> *"O Jabir! Have you just got married?" I said, "Yes." He said, "A virgin or a matron?" I replied, "A matron." He said, "Why not a virgin, so that you might play with her and she with you, and you might amuse her and she amuses you." I said, "Abdullah [my father] died and left girls, and I dislike marrying a girl like them, so I married a lady (matron) so that she may look after them." On that he said, "May Allah bless you."*

(Bukhari)

The Lovemaking Sunna Throughout Marriage

In a manner of speaking, by the Prophet's ﷺ standard, genital intercourse is overrated. Obsessing on it is like devouring the icing without the cake. A glutton may be happy to do so, but a true connoisseur will long to enjoy the cake in its totality. We can have sex like a glutton would have food, not knowing nor caring how it affects our humanity or we can take heed of the Prophet's ﷺ example in humanising sex by using its sensual and social elements to reign in the carnal. We shall now paint a broad picture of what a sex life with a "messenger between the two" can look like. We have selected three key time-periods in a marriage, namely the first night, mid-marriage and menopause-andropause to illustrate.

The First Night

Every newlywed wants to remember their first night as the most beautiful ever, but for many husbands and wives to-be — in particular, the wives — associations of marriage consummation with pain and bleeding, can make it a daunting prospect. So, should the virgin couple expect it to be a painful or sweet experience? Or does it mean every couple needs to have prior sexual experience or they should expect consummation to be a night of pain, failure or comedy, as opposed to the night of their dreams?

At the centre of the newlywed's anxieties is the definition of "consummation", which is to seal the marital oath with sexual intercourse. Ironically, making consummation an objective of the first night of sexual exploration places unnecessary and sometimes debilitating pressure on a couple. As well as this pressure, there are the feelings of shyness, awkwardness and doubt that naturally accompany any first-time experience. In themselves, these are factors that would inhibit the build-up of desire for anyone, but add to this the fact that this will be their first introduction to the differences between male and female sexual desires and the first night really can feel like a minefield to navigate. While the husband is usually erect and ready to go, despite his anxiety, vaginal dryness and tightness are common symptoms of nerves in the wife. This makes pleasurable intercourse practically impossible for her, which in turn makes her even more anxious, dampening whatever desire she may have been harbouring. At this point, the husband, in a sincere attempt to remedy the situation, may be applying all that he knows about stimulation in an effort to excite his wife. Unfortunately, this overwhelming assault on her body only serves to tense her up psycho-emotionally – which is not good for her desire. His perceived lack of success will affect his self-confidence and very possibly, his own desire. Hence, a very confusing and vicious cycle ensues, turning their night of dreams into a nightmare.

This all too common scenario may lead to one of several possible outcomes. A determined couple may make a pact to bite the bullet and force the issue, be it on that very night or a few nights after. Whatever pain and humiliation they suffer, they endure together in the name of love. With perseverance, cooperation and a sense of humour, the initial pain will lessen with time, experience and increasing mutual comfort until the longed-for ideal of sexual bliss becomes the norm. However, we have also encountered couples who have not consummated their vows, even after years of marriage, among our divorce counselling cases. Then, there are the many wives who have never experienced the bliss and intimacy of sex even as they satisfy their husbands out of a sense of duty. Among such husbands there are also those who feel short-changed by their wives' frigidity, even if they have never been deprived of orgasm.

Whatever the outcome may be, most new couples want the first step in their journey of marriage to be the dream night they have been waiting for, but therein lies the problem. The very attempt at achieving a dream encounter usually adds to the couple's anxiety and loss of spontaneity which inevitably has a negative impact on their desire and performance. All things considered, at least for the very first encounter while both parties are new to each other in many senses, it is probably wise not to attempt the consummation. Instead, in line with "the lovemaking sunna" we discussed above, approach the first night with the following points in mind:

1. Forget about sex: First of all, redefine "the first night" to mean a timeframe in which to acquaint yourselves with each other, as opposed to being a specific night for consummating your marriage with intercourse. This suggestion is based on a hadith reported by Ibn Majah, "For the widow, three nights and for the virgin seven nights."

　　　　　　　　　　　　　　　　　　SEX, SOUL AND ISLAM

This means new couples need time to be comfortable being intimate with each other, even for those who are sexually experienced. Even for a widow, the Prophet 🕮 suggested at least three nights and for the virgin he suggested an entire week. Either way, intercourse need not happen that very first night.

Instead, you should treat the "first nights" as a period of discovery. Even if you have already known one another for years during courting, upon marriage you must upgrade your level of understanding and the first nights of marriage provide the perfect opportunity to re-learn or learn more about each other's views, inclinations, ambitions, fears, hopes and idiosyncrasies. Discuss important topics like family, career, housing and further education as well as more light-hearted things like hobbies. Even if you have covered these issues before, the difference now is that you must begin forming some idea of how and when to make these happen together as a couple. Symbolically, your first encounter as husband and wife is the perfect occasion to reintroduce yourselves. Practically, it is an excellent idea to get your hearts and minds closer to each other rather than to sex.

At first glance, this may seem somewhat counter-intuitive to sexual intimacy. But our counselling experience with pregnant unwed teenagers tells us otherwise. Most of them would tell us that the first time sex happened, they never intended to do it. Sex was far from their mind. It usually started with being alone and simply talking which led to friendly banter, then frolicking, then heavy petting, and when it eventually happened, there was no pain or bleeding like we often hear from adult married first-timers.

We do not condone their behaviour, of course. Nevertheless, we cannot deny that their anecdotes illustrate exactly the kind of slow build-up which makes lovemaking mutually pleasurable. For that matter, this is also why Islam is so strictly against close proximity between non-*mahrams* as discussed in Chapter One. But if we can recognise and detest the sin, lawfully married couples can adopt this approach in their own sexual encounters throughout marriage, starting from the first night.

From the point of view of establishing the "messenger between the two", intellectual and emotional connection is far more important than clueless forays into each other's bodies before husband and wife are ready. This is a better approach towards establishing real long-term intimacy, starting from the honeymoon onwards.

2. Honeymoon wisely: A honeymoon is not an Islamic requirement per se nor a recommended sunna, but it is not contradictory to Islamic teachings. If you have the time and resources, it can help with the bonding process, but there are some things you should consider when planning one.

To begin with, avoid holidays that consist of hectic itineraries, extreme adventures or a lot of physical exertion. A round-the-world cycling trip or mountain climbing holiday is not what you should be going for. Any journey is testing on patience and compatibility even among the closest of travelling buddies especially if it is the first time you are travelling together. The punishing challenges of extreme adventures combined with the teething problems of getting to know a new companion at an extremely intimate level are not conducive to an ideal honeymoon environment. Besides, what needs exploring on a honeymoon are each other's minds, bodies and souls. The rest of the world can wait.

Arguably, holiday resorts are the best option for newlyweds. They provide facilities and activities either onsite or nearby meaning couples can devote more time to having fun together rather than travelling between locations. Having the distraction of activities keeps any over-eagerness for sex at bay and allows couples to discover each other on many different levels. Furthermore, should annoying habits and tendencies surface for the first time, they are more likely to be addressed with understanding and an open heart given the great time husband and wife are having together. The choice to take or leave activities in a resort also means that couples can carve out much needed time for intimacy and relaxation.

3. Get spiritual: There are a number of recommended congregational prayers and supplications for the first night as discussed in Chapter Three. In essence, these spiritual practices are about expressing your gratitude to Allah 🕮 for your marriage and your joint desire to progress spiritually together throughout marriage, starting from that very first night. Practically, it is another aspect of familiarisation in terms of spiritual habits and practices. Bringing the special *salah* into the beautiful atmosphere of the first night makes us experience first-hand the solemnity in the meeting of two souls in love under the blessings of Allah 🕮.

As minds, hearts and souls become comfortable, the intimacy of the meeting is enriched. Shyness and awkwardness melt away naturally and genuine mutual desire for physical proximity and contact grows from both parties. Yet, this is precisely when couples must remember the Prophet's 🕮 warning against falling upon each other.

4. Remember the messenger: If you put the above points into practice, you are already following the Prophet's 🕮 example. During all those recreational and spiritual activities, you will have interacted in sensual, emotional, intellectual and spiritual terms. Only through such connections can our carnal desires be stopped from spoiling the slow build-up towards a true person-to-person intimacy. In following the recommendations of the Messenger of Allah 🕮, you should bring language into the vocabulary of sex early in the marriage. It is perhaps the best time to get closer to the topic of sex, starting with the topics we discussed above. But, if intellectual discussions bore you, get cheeky and tease each other

Men tend to **miss** the **forest** for the **trees** when they become **obsessed** with their wife's **body parts** over her as a **total** person but couples too **suffer** from this delusion when they develop a habit of intimacy which is **confined** to pure **genital** intercourse.

with what orgasm could be like. It doesn't matter what you talk about: the point is to bring language into your vocabulary of sex early on.

This makes you comfortable to verbalise as you begin to explore each other's bodies sensually, just as an art-lover would as he explores a tactile piece of art like sculpture or pottery. Take your time and relish the very act of undressing your lover, moan and sigh deliberately as you relieve the heavy pounding of your heart, feast your eyes lingeringly on every little detail as it is unveiled and mutter your praises as every praise is music to your lover's ears.

Touch, caress, massage, feel, kiss, lick, smell, listen and be pleasured by God's favourite work of art; the human body. Describe what is going on in your heart and mind as you do so. Ask what is going on in your lover's mind. Do not assume. Ask your spouse what they enjoy and listen when they tell you what they do not want. Learn to request, feedback, suggest, clarify and communicate in ways which do not spoil the passion and romance. Most importantly, make the effort to ensure the sensual pleasuring is mutual. Only then, when you are truly at ease in each other's company, will advances towards the private parts be welcomed and enjoyed.

5. Who calls the shots? Sayyiduna Ali ﴿ said that women possess nine parts of desire compared to men's one part. Those desires are veiled in nine parts of shyness whereas a man's shyness is measured as one part. The "messenger between the two" is not going to change this reality. It may close the gap between their differences as it calms the bold one while it coaxes the coy as they play on the plateau of human pleasures, but in truth, there is bound to be confusion, apprehension and lots of second-guessing along the way.

Should the husband take the lead as he is the more adventurous or will his forthrightness rush him towards climax? Will her natural reticence keep better pace for them as they discover a new experience together or will it bring both parties to nowhere? To resolve this dilemma, the principle of husbandly leadership and wifely stewardship is all the more relevant here, in this most intimate moment of early marriage. Men's forthrightness will have to play a leading role in charting the way forward. However, it is not leadership by command and certainly not by force. It is leadership by example that is valuable: one that requires him to empathise with her state of readiness even as he charts the way forward. Yet, the wife's responsive involvement is just as important.

To use urban metaphors: if the husband were a pilot, the wife is the control tower; if he were a space explorer, she is mission control on earth; if he were the sports star, she is the coach who prepares and guides him on how the game should be played on that particular day. In all of these metaphors, it is quite difficult to say who calls the shots. What is certain is their success depends heavily on their chemistry as each plays his and her respective parts well. While the husband's candour is needed to keep the exploration going, the deciding factor as to where it should go and how fast it should get there depends on the wife's readiness. As good leaders do, he should take the cue from the wife on such matters. During these first nights, a husband more than ever needs to reign in the fierce sexual urges that rage in him, to give way to the gentleman.

As a rule of thumb, the sweetest consummation happens when she voluntarily invites him into her – free from his suggestions, coaxes, pressures and especially from coercion. This is because her voluntary invitation only comes when she is psycho-emotionally ready for arousal. It is under such favourable conditions that a pleasurable, memorable consummation takes place. In contrast are the husbands throwing tantrums over their wife's menstruation during honeymoon. There could be nothing more heart-breaking for a bride, than to discover such unchivalrous attitudes from her knight in shining armour. Such behaviour will not only spoil the honeymoon, it is bound to spoil the sexual dynamics of the marriage. On the other hand, for couples who embrace the Prophet's 🕌 "messenger" hadith, being deprived of intercourse, be it for religious or personal reasons, will not be an issue as the first nights are about establishing heart-to-heart intimacy.

Please note however, the five points above are not meant to be a step-by-step checklist. Rather, they are points to remember. One may overtake the other, or even be ignored if it is necessary. The overarching aim of this process is for couples to attune themselves with the other before the animality of sex spoils the first night experience and worse still, follows through into mid-marriage routines.

Mid-marriage Grind

We use "mid-marriage" to refer loosely to married life after the honeymoon all the way through to the golden years. During this period, love, romance and sex jostle with the chaos of daily living for the couple's attention. You may return to a mounting backlog of inquiries and late nights at the office directly following the honeymoon, except that you now have a commitment to your spouse to consider. With time, the demands on your attention will increase and yet, the number of hours in a day remains unchanged.

Increasing fatigue and the grinding routine of making ends meet may lead couples to consider the Prophet's 🕌 "messenger" as too idealistic a concept to uphold. Given their lack of energy and enthusiasm, they may find it more expedient to go straight for the quickies to get their conjugal duties over and done with and the sensual pleasuring and socialising the Prophet 🕌 advocated may now have become a burden. Similar observations have been made by sex therapists too:

Courting couples usually cannot wait to enjoy each other's touch. But, after a time, too many couples look upon some kinds of sustained touch, such as holding hands, as being adolescent, silly, or embarrassing. Too many couples restrict their affectionate touch only to sexual intercourse, depriving themselves of the enriching closeness produced by holding and being held.

(Domeena Renshaw)[77]

In sex counselling, some men object to what they call "all that touchy-feely garbage." They say it's just an excuse to put off sex used by women who feel squeamish about "getting it on".

(Michael Castleman)[78]

It appears the tendency to cut down sexual interaction to its most basic level as couples grow familiar with one another is a common theme uniting both East and West. Some resort to this type of union out of sheer laziness, misplaced machismo or general misconceptions about sex. However, there are some who truly succumb to the pressures of daily living. These pressures are compounded when couples rely heavily on functional sex to maintain an illusion of intimacy. From there on in, they drift apart even as they maintain the façade of a marriage. In such instances, some people may find alternative or supplementary relief through masturbation, pornography and in the most extreme scenarios, with the involvement of a third party; even if these options are, in reality, as perfunctory as the sex with their partner.

We must concede that there are also couples or individuals who are truly not bothered by a perfunctory sex life. There are many other aspects of marriage they can be satisfied with in place of sexual gratification. Such people may be capable of experiencing a fulfilling marriage despite the monotony of sex. In these instances, their choices are perfectly valid if they are truly happy with them. More concerning are the couples who unknowingly ruin their marriage and sex-life because they fail to see the connection between bad marital relations and bad sexual relations. As a result, they take short-cuts to sex, abandoning the longer but surer route mapped out by the Prophet ﷺ towards a marriage made up of love and intimacy. Unfortunately, this is the recurrent theme manifested in various presenting problems among couples we have counselled on marital dysfunction. The following are typical examples of these problems. We have separated them for ease of discussion, but in reality, they are often intertwined.

The wife is not interested: Despite both modern scientific findings and traditional wisdom touting women as having the superior sexual prowess, many husbands' perception is quite the opposite. More often in counselling, we hear husbands complaining of wives losing interest in sex than the other way around. Yet only in very rare cases is this due to what is perceived to be women's supposed nature. More often, the female's low libido is due to a simple logical reason which somehow escapes the notice of their partner.

In counselling, we have witnessed many cases of working wives, coupled with unsupportive husbands, who could not cope with the demands of a full-time job, housework, children and sex. Some husbands genuinely cannot understand why these chores should affect sexual desire. When it is time for sex – so he thinks – the candles, perfumes, music and his swanky own good looks will put her back in the mood, hot, sexy and all over him. In truth, such gestures are immaterial if the wife resents the injustice of her situation. What hurts her most is his apathy to her plight. A wife's sexual desire is determined by one question: do I want to be with this man tonight? If the answer is yes, there is no limit to what she will offer of herself, but it is unlikely to be yes if she feels resentful, angry or disappointed in her spouse.

In *Why Men Don't Have a Clue and Women Always Need More Shoes!* Alan and Barbara Pease explain, "Unlike a man, (a woman) doesn't use a man's appearance and grooming as a measure of how he feels about her. Instead, she measures his love by how he treats her."[79] Among the cases we have encountered, many men are struck by a simple point we often make in explaining their failed sexual advances towards their wives: "if she is not happy with you, she cannot make you happy". After dealing with many such cases, we note there are bigger forces like social norms, family upbringing or religious interpretations concealing many men from this simple truth.

During one session of mandatory divorce counselling a husband touted his wife's sexual refusals as a presenting problem. However, the wife's rejections stemmed from her husband's verbal abuse of her and the children to the extent of wishing her Hell in the Hereafter. He was not physically abusive nor was he unfaithful, he provided for the family and was religious and responsible in all other ways. Considering his compliance to his other husbandly duties, in his opinion, the husband's unkindness paled in comparison to her refusal of his conjugal rights.

It is typical that while refusal of sex is considered the ultimate *nushuz* or recalcitrant disobedience, the warning to be kind is regarded as a soft moral reminder and not as grave a commandment as the former. Interestingly though, both commandments actually appear in the Quran and hadith without ranking. If they were taken in totality without bias, a verbally unkind husband should be as guilty of *nushuz* as the wife who refuses him. Her failure to fulfil her duties is feeding off her husband's failure to be kind and vice-versa.

Unfortunately, this is an all too typical example of when a legal right afforded by the *sharia* is wrongly prioritised at the expense of *akhlaq* in our observance of Islam. In the case of marriage, it obscures the simple truth about female desire: if a man's wife is not happy with him, she cannot gratify him with sincerity, even if she would like to. She may bring her body to bed out of religious duty, but she cannot force it to perform, not when her husband's behaviour towards her gives her mind and soul no cause to yearn for his presence. Thus, the husband's lust may be temporarily sated, but without the participation of their minds and souls, both husband and wife remain unsatisfied.

There are also a significant number of cases where the wife's unhappiness with the husband is not always of his making. We have encountered a wife who was unjustly disdainful of her husband's lack of professional ambition to the point of it affecting her desire for him. We have also counselled a number of wives who were unreasonably critical of their husbands' standard of housework with the fussing, nagging and fatigue jointly spoiling both their desires for intimacy.

Whatever the reason for a wife's rejection, it often has little to do with her natural biological condition. Once that is acknowledged by both parties, they recognise that no medical solution is adequate. Long, difficult and sometimes painful counselling sessions are needed to help the couple understand the causes for her lack of libido. Only then can husband and wife begin to plan concrete steps towards regaining marital bliss including its sexual dimensions. Unfortunately for some couples, the damage is so great that parting is inevitable. In such cases, counselling can help prepare them for a better start in a future relationship.

As for newly married couples, failure and pain can be avoided if they start their marriage on the right footing by embracing the Prophet's ﷺ call to establish the "messenger between the two". Through "words of love" husband and wife can establish an open and positive channel of communication through which any issues can be identified and addressed, be they sexual or otherwise, as we know that more general marital problems can have a knock-on effect in the bedroom.

Common sexual dysfunctions: The connection between bad sex and wider marital unhappiness is evident in many common sexual problems that occur in mid-marriage. These include but are not limited to: premature ejaculation (PE) and erectile dysfunction (ED) among men and penetration difficulties (vaginismus) and inability to have orgasms among women. Unfortunately, couples routinely side-step or even hide such issues during marriage counselling, believing they have little to do with their daily interactions. However, if left untreated, sexual problems can easily undo whatever progress has been made in marital counselling. A marriage must be viewed holistically if dysfunctions are to be effectively addressed. Couples

SEX, SOUL AND ISLAM

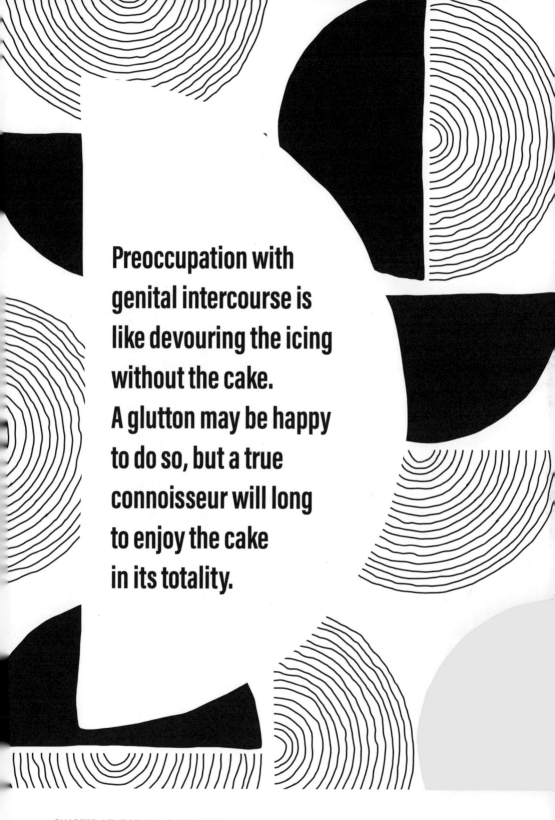

Preoccupation with genital intercourse is like devouring the icing without the cake. A glutton may be happy to do so, but a true connoisseur will long to enjoy the cake in its totality.

who appreciate how the emotional tensions between them can affect their sexual satisfaction are less likely to need marital counselling in the first place.

There are many sex therapists highlighting the non-physical causes of sexual dysfunctions. For example, some assert that physical causes of PE are truly uncommon,[80] only 35% of ED is caused by physical factors,[81] vaginismus is chiefly emotionally triggered[82] and women unable to achieve orgasm do not often show signs of any physical abnormality.[83] Undeniably, there are cases involving genital deformities or functional deterioration requiring medical and surgical intervention, but these are rare. Intangible factors like negative emotions, psychological issues and misinformation are often at the root of sexual dysfunctions.

A typical example of how such factors work surreptitiously to cause real damage is a man who get unnecessarily anxious when his erection is a little slow to come on or less pronounced due to common fatigue, family crisis or age. Some men jump to the conclusion that they are on the verge of losing their sexual ability completely and they begin comparing notes with friends who are bound to share exaggerated accounts of their own prowess. The problem is then escalated further when they start blaming their wife for not being able to arouse them anymore, which in turn affects her self-esteem or triggers combative two-way blame-games. As a result, anxiety, fear, embarrassment, anger and confusion become the collective cause of real erectile dysfunction. Like a self-fulfilling prophecy, a man's unfounded anxiety over a perceived problem can cause that problem to materialise and manifest itself in a much more serious fashion.

Interestingly, Michael Castleman explained stress-related erection problems in terms of the fight-or-flight reflex which occurs naturally within a human being under threat, causing the blood to draw away from the centre of the body towards the limbs in preparation for self-defence or escape.[84] In other words, a flaccid penis under the circumstances described above is working in perfect harmony with a perfectly functioning human body and is not something to worry about. It is the circumstances that need to change. For the same reason, a man's anxiety over his ability to last long enough in lovemaking is a major contributor to PE.[85] Vaginismus is also an entirely natural protective reflex triggered by traumatic experiences but it is reversible.[86] Similarly, performance anxiety in a woman, often rooted in social misconceptions regarding women's sexuality– whether they are traditional ideas of women's inborn frigidity to modern-day expectations of women's sexual liberty – can present itself in her inability to orgasm.[87]

Sexual dysfunctions involve both physical and psycho-emotional complications which require case-by-case assessment by a sex-specialist, ideally. Yet, despite all our advancements in understanding problems with sexual performance, there is still a stigma attached to seeking professional help. For this reason, many people turn to anonymous quick-fixes from coffee-shop experts and back-street suppliers for aphrodisiacs, sex drugs, numbing creams and lubricants to solve their self-diagnosed sexual problems, but such solutions can do no more than correct genital shortcomings without addressing the psycho-emotional and relational issues that cause them in the first place. In contrast, sex therapists may not even rely on medicines or surgery when treating PE and ED, because the problem is often not with the penis. Nor do they rely on psychiatry either as these are hardly mental illnesses. Rather, as these symptoms are more due to misinformation, sex therapy is akin to coaching. Patients are guided to unlearn the errors and relearn the right way towards lovemaking, as explained by Domeena Renshaw:

> Sex therapy combines sex education and relationship therapy with sexual activities at home (I call it home loveplay), which progresses weekly from caressing without touching the genitals all the way to intercourse ... Many sexual problems arise from sexual misinformation – or no information at all. Sex education and home loveplay can help couples "unlearn" unsatisfying sexual behaviour.[88]

Ultimately, what restores lost sexual bliss is the expansion of the intimate experience beyond the carnal – but not excluding it – towards the full spectrum of human intimacy through the agency of "extended sensuality". As Michael Castleman points out:

> Many men's preoccupation with "the old in-out" traps them in a no-win situation – they develop sex problems, and their lovers become frustrated. Extended sensuality, on the other hand, is the key to no-lose lovemaking. Men are more likely to become the lovers they would like to be and women are more likely to become the lovers men would like them to be.[89]

Similarly, the Prophet ﷺ warned Muslim husbands not to "fall suddenly upon (their) wife like an animal." The "kissing and words of love" that the Prophet ﷺ highlights are the rudiments of extended sensuality through which the tranquillity, love and mercy extolled in *Al-Rum 30:21*, are achieved. Without "the messenger between the two" the act of "mating" is focused solely on the genitals, giving rise to male-female disharmony. Once these strong foundations are laid, sexual and marital bliss must be consciously maintained and, hopefully, enhanced as we continually learn, discover and enrich our lovemaking vocabulary.

Underestimating the logistics of lovemaking: In films and music videos, when a couple makes love, everything falls into place. In real life though, even the hands need some organising during spooning to make sure they don't go numb, the stones, twigs and insects on the rock by the brook need sweeping away before the damsel may swoon on it under her lover and as reel lovers frolic day and night, real lovers have to work. In truth, it takes a lot of discipline, organisation and problem solving to make romantic, passionate sex a regular feature of marriage. A couple have to take proactive and concrete steps to create a home environment and pattern of daily activity which will be conducive to romance. This does not require a grand master plan, but rather sensitivity and responsiveness to the small things that threaten to hinder romance on a long-term basis.

Amongst our clients was a couple who had not engaged in intercourse since their first child was born seven years prior. The wife felt uncomfortable having sex with the child sleeping in the room and so, their first homework was to remove "the elephant in the room". Thankfully, it was not too difficult as they were open to the ideas and pointers given. Unfortunately, couples wrecking their sexual life due to unassertive parenting is all too common.

There are, of course, couples who are genuinely exhausted by work, despite managing their time as effectively as they can. It may be that one partner is at a pivotal time in their career or both partners are working shifts which are not compatible with each other. Typically, when one party is rested, the other is still exhausted and so, a lack of time and energy combine with desire mismatch to make couple time a frustrating affair. Ironically, this is when a more calculative and logical approach must be taken to revive romance and passion.

When faced with a situation which feels overwhelming, one of the best things a couple can do is not fight against it, but go with the flow. For couples who were always too exhausted after a day at the office or looking after the children, we suggested they succumb to their fatigue and go to sleep instead of trying to force a romance. Fatigue-induced sleep is usually deep and restful which can leave many people waking up refreshed in the dead of night. By making the effort to wake before dawn, freshen up and set the scene for romance, couples can take advantage of a window of opportunity as the world (including their children) sleeps. After enjoying their intimate time, the couple can bathe together and perform *Fajr* prayer, giving them the best possible start to their day.

It is also useful for couples who lack time and energy not to fixate on intercourse. For example, following a night shift at work, a partner's sexual advances can actually be irritating as the exhausted spouse craves sleep and rest. In turn, the one who initiates sex may feel frustrated with the other's unresponsiveness. This nega-

Unlike a man, **a woman** doesn't use a man's **appearance** and **grooming** as a measure of how he **feels** about her. Instead, she measures his **love** by how he **treats** her.

ALAN AND BARBARA PEASE,
*WHY MEN DON'T HAVE A CLUE AND WOMEN
ALWAYS NEED MORE SHOES!*

tive dynamic can be altered if intercourse is taken out of the equation. Instead, the rested partner can help the one who is tired to relax, unwind and destress with the clever use of massage or other types of touch. Even if it ends with one party asleep, it is far better than regularly frustrating attempts at sex. More importantly, as the giver enjoys the beloved's body while the beloved is soothed to sleep, they will grow comfortable and accustomed to touching and being touched all over the body. It makes for a far better lovemaking experience on those rare occasions where the couple can accommodate a proper sexual union. Admittedly, this approach can be difficult as it calls for a generous giving heart without the expectation of payback, a personal quality advocated by Paul Scott in *Sensual Massage*:

> **Make your massage a gift:** *put your lover at ease. Explain to them you are doing this because you want to, and not because you expect a massage in return. Give it for the sake of giving. Only then can they be able to focus on themselves and become completely relaxed. If they want to return the favour, they can do so another day.*
>
> *Although massage techniques can be part of foreplay, however, it is vital never to begin a massage with the assumption that it will end in intercourse. Asking your lover for sex or trying to "get them going" will undo all your good work, resulting in your partner feeling stressed and resisting your favour.[90]*

But if couples can acquire that attitude, they will find the regular act of gifting sensations very achievable. In fact, it is so intuitive to us as humans that it was developed into the art of massage in so many traditional cultures of both the East and the West where it is a common act of service among friends, family members and of course, lovers. An expert skill set is not required. Simple massage techniques to relieve tired muscles, soothe tense joints and destress the mind can be easily mastered to make the pleasures of touch, and the other senses, our daily offering to each other.

Sometimes, putting your heads together, brainstorming with responsible friends or researching ideas in sex therapy books is enough to address the glitches threatening the romance of your marriage, but if the relationship has become too strained, professional help may be needed. Either way, when logistical issues arise, they must be actively addressed, not brushed aside and not regarded as the end of marital romance. Planning is key because, in the hustle and bustle of daily living, romantic opportunities do not appear out of the blue.

Complacency over physical appearance: The element of visual pleasure is not to be underestimated when discussing extended sensuality. Surely, for the human body to be a source of visual delight it has to be in prime condition or it can become a desire killer instead? But the pursuit of the ideal body is controversial as it has undeniably contributed to eating disorders, indiscriminate abuse of surgeries, self-esteem issues and the shallow pursuit of gratification through materialism. Issues with appearance are not limited to newlyweds. Many couples in mid-marriage come up against such problems at some point. This is no surprise, as a marriage generally involves two people who were once physically attracted to each other, especially among "love marriages".

For example, it is common for many middle-aged women we have counselled to express their hurt at a husband's terse remarks about weight gain or unkind comparisons with the wife's appearance in her youth. Often, this figures as a smaller, less important side-issue to wider problems, but it is a significant contributor to friction within a marriage. Often, the complaining husband's appearance has been equally altered by time and lifestyle, but the wife usually prioritises his words and behaviour over his physical deterioration. This only serves to compound the issue as the wife cannot comprehend her husband's inability to accept her imperfections just as she accepts his. The husband, in turn, believes he is just being open and honest, even as he admits to his own double standards.

The frequency with which this so-called side-issue crops up in our sessions makes us suspect it is not such a side-issue after all. Even among couples where physical appearance does not threaten the solid foundations of their marriage, the issue may still crop up as friendly banter, to be brushed aside as soon as it gets uncomfortable. Many couples do not want to address it, not because they cannot see it but rather they fear upsetting the delicate harmony over a purportedly shallow or petty issue. On the one hand, they acknowledge the vanity and shallowness of such material concerns as skin care, hair maintenance and weight loss. However, they cannot deny that as they lose their looks to age, looking at each other is not as pleasurable as it once was. So, for better or worse, they switch off the lights and do it in the dark. When the focus shifts from all the sensual pleasures to genital intercourse alone, who cares about looks? And who cares about one obscure *sunna* about, "kissing and words of love"? This is when the issue of physical appearance begins to impact all areas of the marriage.

At this point, it is important to consider that physical fitness has other facets besides looks and grooming. If we look at it through the lens of Islam, the body is one of the means given to the vicegerent of God along with wealth, intelligence and power. Therefore, it follows that mankind has a duty to look after it and use it wisely. In spite of this, the global Muslim community is worryingly neglectful of the importance of physical health in serving Allah ﷻ on Earth.[91] The prevailing trend amongst married couples reflects this communal complacency.

There is, however, no valid reason for not prioritising the human body in the scheme of Islamic development. Considering it vain or shallow is false piety as Islamic teachings are replete with commandments to look after our bodies through eating well, restraining desires, eschewing luxuries and being physically active.

> The Prophet ﷺ once "saw a man in a vision, so he ﷺ called him and he
> came and he ﷺ told him about it. And he had a large belly, so he ﷺ said
> with his finger on the belly, "if this were in a different place than this it
> would be better for you."

(Tabrani)

In light of this hadith, displeasure at a spouse's weight gain may not be that shallow after all. It may, in fact, be an intuitive reaction against this bodily form of neglect and misuse just as we might feel unease over the deliberate neglect and misuse of God-given intellect, wealth or power. We say this not in support of the insensitive husband or wife who judges their spouse with cruel words and unkind actions even as they too have neglected their own fitness. Clearly, their purpose is motivated towards their selfish personal enjoyment. Nor is it meant to pressure those who are genuinely beyond their capacity to keep fit due to valid medical and congenital reasons. Rather, for couples who are confused, divided, conflicted or ambivalent about keeping in shape, this is a more productive stance to work from.

With this viewpoint in mind, every couple – be it young or old, veteran or newly-wed, slim or obese – can choose to strive as a family in keeping the body in shape out of a sense of duty towards a God-given trust, because it is the striving itself that generates respect, admiration and camaraderie among them, rather than the perfect body image. An attractive appearance acquired through quick-fixes like cosmetic surgery, steroids or extreme dieting are not lasting solutions and are often viewed as desperate or extreme by other family members. In contrast, healthy eating, controlling impulses and desires and a physically active lifestyle are all goals which a family can pursue and benefit from, together. The improvements to fitness, strength, stamina and appearance is a bonus to the enhanced intimacy which arises out of a shared journey.

Banking on sex for intimacy: The cases discussed above show that sex is not a guaranteed path towards intimacy as it can also be a source of conflict. Sex merely amplifies what you bring into the relationship. When the entire human entity is involved in mutually connecting and pleasuring each other, the sex binds, but when it is approached for selfish gratification, sex divides as incompatibilities are amplified by the very sensations and emotions that are supposed to unite. We shall look at why this is the case from the angle of intimacy.

Human intimacy refers to person-to-person closeness, attachment or comfort and it has as many facets as a human being does. Therefore, a truly human intimacy involves the intellectual, emotional, social, spiritual and the physical.

Intellectual intimacy refers to a couple's comfort in sharing their ideas, opinions, viewpoints and even raw, unpolished thoughts about anything that comes into their mind. It is not about matching intellectual capacity but rather being at ease in expressing thoughts without fear of ridicule, judgment or anger. In order to achieve intellectual intimacy, couples should assure each other in words and gestures that their thoughts are always welcome; even in cases of differing intellectual capability or levels of education. In such an instance, the more educated of the two should listen patiently, clarify what they mean and if needed, correct their partner in a reassuring manner. For those who are intellectually matched, they must be careful not to challenge each other excessively, leading to an environment of antagonism. Intellectual intimacy must be honed through long discussions, starting from early marriage and during which, husband and wife can share their innermost thoughts and feelings with each other. By doing so, a couple will inevitably reveal paths to the other facets of intimacy.

The meeting of minds opens the door to the meeting of hearts through empathy and this is what we call emotional intimacy. Again, it is the ability to find common ground, but also to reconcile differences in what makes each person happy, sad, excited, bored and so on. In contrast, there are couples who bottle-up or tip-toe around each other's feelings or impose their own emotional values forcefully, creating tension and resentment. They are not free to feel, think and act for fear of a negative reaction from their partner. Intellectual intimacy, open communication and even professional help may be required for the "meeting of hearts", but the journey must begin with a sincere intention to allow your spouse into your heart.

Social intimacy is about feeling comfortable in each other's presence in social situations, whether you are among relatives, friends or peers. The opposite, social alienation – be it due to wealth, upbringing, education, race, caste or beliefs – is a favourite theme of many love stories because it is relatable for those who have felt the pain of not belonging. Therefore, we root for the lovers as they struggle against these artificial barriers together. In reality, couples can avoid the hurt of social alienation by spending a lot of time together and sharing interests. If one spouse spends considerable time with other groups of people due to different interests or demanding careers, it is wise to introduce and acquaint the other partner to that group, wherever suitable, before the external social circle becomes a pull factor against their intimacy.

Spiritual intimacy is possibly the most overlooked aspect of a couple's relationship. Differences in levels of piety, ritual norms and religious interpretations can affect the dynamics of a relationship. Cases we have come across include: A practising wife who no longer found her non-practising husband desirable, a club-going husband and his mosque-going wife failing to find common interests and a couple who drifted apart after the husband joined a spiritual sect. Though these are the extremes, spiritual differences can test even the strongest marriages. Hence, spiritual practices in Islam always have a congregational or *jamaat* element to help couples and their families grow spiritually together.

In contrast, physical intimacy is what most married couples are familiar with, at least in early marriage. For newlyweds, to touch, look and hear each other is exhilarating and they treasure these sensations, using them to express their love and longing. Unfortunately, there are many couples who neglect physical intimacy later into the marriage, often viewing it as a poor cousin to sexual intimacy which involves their naked bodies and genitals. If husband and wife are able to feel the same connection as physical intimacy during sexual intercourse, it is indeed the most intense, profound and mind-blowing form of intimacy, but most people abandon physical intimacy for all the wrong reasons, as discussed earlier. Inevitably, sexual intimacy also suffers.

The above categorisations of intimacy are not exhaustive. Some couples may experience aspects very specific to them like creative, recreational or professional intimacy. The important thing is to be aware of what applies to your relationship. We have encountered several cases of couples drifting apart when decisions around career and education left one party feeling inferior or excluded. In some cases, their spiritual and physical intimacies are strong enough to pull them together despite their differences, but in others, the push factor from these incompatibilities is too great. When that happens, it is genuinely puzzling to them as they have failed to make the connection between these neglected areas and their otherwise healthy relationship.

As we have learnt, physical intimacy is just one of the many facets of intimacy and sexual closeness is just one sub-set of that. Thus, banking on sex, especially perfunctory sex, for marital intimacy is like relying on a star striker who is at logger-heads with his disunited football team, to win a game. Win or lose, it will not be an enjoyable game and wherever sex is involved, if it is not fun, nobody wins. Sex is like a highly skilled player which will only be an asset if other team members can play well enough and all can play as one. Couples need to be aware of the other team members of intimacy and develop them adequately so that sex can work its magic in intensifying a comprehensive intimacy between them.

In summary, bringing the "messenger" into your mid-marriage sex-life is not about eschewing intercourse – that would be unrealistic, unproductive and not in keeping with Islamic values which see sexual intercourse and the elements of intimacy including tranquillity, love and mercy as intertwined (Ar-Rum 30:21). Instead, it is about taking the focus and thus the pressure away from sexual intercourse. If it happens, embrace it. If it does not, make an active effort to enjoy all categories of intimacy in the meantime. This way, when the time for intercourse is right, it is not forced or rushed, but a powerful bonding experience.

Sex in the Golden Years

There are very specific clinical definitions of menopause and andropause, but for our purpose a conceptual understanding will be sufficient. Menopause refers to a stage where a woman is no longer fertile, indicated by the cessation of menstruation, usually between the ages of forty-five and fifty-five. Relevant to our discussion are its common symptoms including hot-flushes, weight-gain, vaginal dryness and other bothersome bodily discomforts. These physical changes can affect a woman psychologically, causing her to feel depressed, angry or anxious. None of these symptoms are conducive to arousing female sexual desire and in instances where sex was already a chore, it is now torture.

Andropause is slightly controversial as even the experts cannot agree whether this male equivalent of menopause exists from a biological point of view. Nevertheless, around that same age-bracket, many men experience the proverbial mid-life crisis causing them to re-examine their priorities, perceptions and direction in life. Many also experience an apparent reduction in sexual interest and potency coinciding with these changes. Whether or not and to what extent andropause happens differs between men depending on their health, fitness, genetics and state of mind. Given the sexual upheavals these changes bring about in both men and women, it is understandable that many couples misconstrue these phenomena as a cue for sexual retirement.

A reduction in the frequency, ease and duration of penile erections naturally occurs during middle-age, but such changes can be a great source of anxiety for men who expect their sexual potency to remain as it was in their youth. If in younger days erections could be triggered easily and sometimes, for no apparent reason, they now require deliberate, sustained stimulation – be it visual, imaginative, or through touch. Considering that sustained pleasuring is conducive to lovemaking anyway, there is no need for a husband to feel anxious about his reliance on them.

But rather than exploring different ways of stimulation with their wife, often a man will instead turn to quick fixes like Viagra. At the same time, this anxiety worsens due to false comparisons with bragging friends and the myths around male prowess churned out by the advertising and porn industries.

Unfortunately, much of the time, andropausal husbands care little for their wives' feelings as they battle with their own menopause. We witnessed a divorce case involving an elderly couple where the husband had discovered a newfound virility and potency after a visit to a village medicine man whereas his wife was struggling with vaginal dryness and general frailty. The sex had never been enjoyable for her, but now his energetic advances and his rush towards intercourse, had become torturous for her. Having endured bad sex for many years, having born and raised his children and tolerated his selfish, uncaring ways, she felt she had done more than what a wife can be expected to do and wanted out.

It is a pity that mid-life biological changes in men and women end up ruining a relationship of many years, when, with a little knowledge and understanding, couples can use such changes to their advantage, as an opportunity to achieve a more varied sexual experience. In his book *He Comes Next – The Thinking Woman's Guide to Pleasuring a Man,* Dr Ian Kerner explains that:

> ... so many couples in their fifties and sixties ... insist that the sex they're having now is better than ever before ... They also say that sex has become more creative and tender, less orgasm driven, more sensual, and ultimately intimate. Some of this has to do with the fact that as men age, their testosterone levels decrease, while estrogen levels increase. So, he's naturally discovering a softer side of sex. The men who are the happiest are the ones who ultimately accept and embrace these natural changes and discover new paths in their sexual journey.[92]

What this tells us is that the positive aspects of andropausal change will not be discovered by couples who focus their sexual activities around intercourse. On the contrary, if the "messenger" has been an active presence in their marriage, with a focus on mutual pleasuring, seduction vocabulary and building up chemistry over a number of years, losing an erection will not be regarded a disaster, but instead a sign of how relaxed and comfortable he is with his body in her presence. This relaxation allows him to focus on her pleasure and allows his wife to dictate a slower, gentler pace as she has more control over her husband's arousal. In contrast, anxiety over an intermittent erection can cause an actual erectile dysfunction, as discussed earlier in this chapter.

While **refusal** of sex is considered the ultimate *nushuz* or recalcitrant disobedience, the warning to be **kind** is regarded as a **soft** moral reminder and not as **grave** a commandment as the former. Interestingly though, **both** commandments actually appear in the Quran and hadith **without** ranking.

As for menopausal symptoms, a husband who is familiar with pleasuring will naturally be more emphatic to his wife's discomforts and will be able to draw on a wider repertoire of touches and words to relieve and even heal her pain. If a man accepts the mellowing of his sexual urges and recognises his increased preference towards other forms of sexual intimacy, even vaginal dryness becomes a minor issue as a sexually confident couple seeks solutions which also stimulate, such as artificially lubricating each other.

In summary, the Prophet's ﷺ lovemaking *sunna* calls for couples to avoid the hasty, direct route towards sexual intercourse as the slow, meandering deliberate path invites different facets of their humanity to show themselves and contribute to the sexual experience. However, we do not want couples to be discouraged by the wrongful assumption that pursuing the prophetic idea of lovemaking requires an overwhelming amount of time and energy. This suggests a compartmentalisation of time into periods of "sex" and "no sex" and betrays the proper understanding of "let there be a messenger between the two" as all time is lovemaking time when it is not confined to genital intercourse. As long as standards of decency are maintained in public and in front of family members, pleasuring your spouse mentally, emotionally and sensually should be part and parcel of daily life.

In conclusion, if both parties feel truly sexually satisfied, couples should not worry if they have gone for weeks on end without sex, or if their fondling and kissing often ends in sleep instead of intercourse. In fact, in a mutually satisfied couple, one partner may even sacrifice their own comfort once in a while to provide sex when their spouse is overly aroused and needs a release. Whatever the frequency, venue or circumstances of sex, if the overall feeling between the spouses is one of sexual satisfaction and mutual understanding in accordance with the Prophet's ﷺ message, they can enjoy a healthy sex life from the honeymoon period, during mid-marriage, right through to the golden years.

Common Myths

Myths pertaining to sex are numerous, but we would like to highlight a few which hinder couples from attaining a mutually shared sexual bliss.

Vaginal Stimulation Triggers Female Orgasm

It is not wrong to expect the female orgasm to correspond to the male orgasm because we are, after all, two versions of the same species. For this reason, it has long been taken for granted that since sexual intercourse stimulates the penis to trigger male orgasm, it should also stimulate the vagina to trigger female orgasm. However, scientific studies reveal that orgasm during vaginal penetration are rare among women.[93] Even before empirical evidence was available, this fact was an open secret in most societies, with some attributing it to women's lower sexual capacity, while others gave the reason as men's lack of skills in controlling orgasm or vaginal stimulation. The obvious conclusion of this thought process was that, if both the man and woman were adequate in sexual skills and capacity, sexual intercourse should generate orgasm for both.

Modern scientific studies show orgasm through clitoral stimulation to be more intense than through intercourse.[94] This suggests the clitoris as the ground-zero of female orgasm. True or false, these findings cannot negate the occurrence of women who have achieved orgasm solely through vaginal intercourse. To confuse the matter further is the discovery in 1950 by Dr Ernest Grafenberg of an erotic spot about halfway down the vaginal canal famously known as the G-spot which could also stimulate an intense orgasm.[95] And so, a debate ensued as to which is the "superior orgasm"; clitoral, vaginal or G-spot? Notable here, is the controversy over the G-spot orgasm with some women swearing by its devastating powers while others insist it does not exist at all. [96]

If this male-female comparison cannot settle the female orgasm debate, it is only because the penis-vagina comparison is not an apple-to-apple comparison, as far as sexual orgasm is concerned. In this case, the female organ that corresponds with the penis is actually not the vagina, but the clitoris. The penis and clitoris begin their formation from the same tissue in a sexless embryo. Later on, in adult men and women, their sensations correspond to each other, except that it is a lot stronger in the clitoris due to its single exclusive function as a centre of pleasure for women.[97] Still, they have one function in common which is that both serve as triggers of sexual climax. The vaginal wall, on the other hand, is largely insensitive.[98] Therefore, female orgasms have always been solely clitoral. Reports of vaginal and G-spot orgasms are in fact cases of mistaken identity, due to the configuration of the clitoris. The pea-sized clitoral head, which is visible near the top of the vaginal opening, is like the proverbial tip of the iceberg. The clitoris is a bigger organ with roots and glands spreading deeper.[99] The famous G-spot sensation actually results from the stimulation of these inner components,[100] but because how deep and far it spreads differs between women, not every stimulator hits the target.

Claimants of vaginal orgasm are also working under a misapprehension. Depending on the couple's unique combination of genitalia size, angle, orientation, shape and location – which are all subtle differences from person to person – knowingly or otherwise, the penis may also stroke the clitoris during the in-out or side-way movements of coital thrusts. In addition, very much like the penis on a man, the clitoris swells when a woman is highly aroused – head, roots, glands and

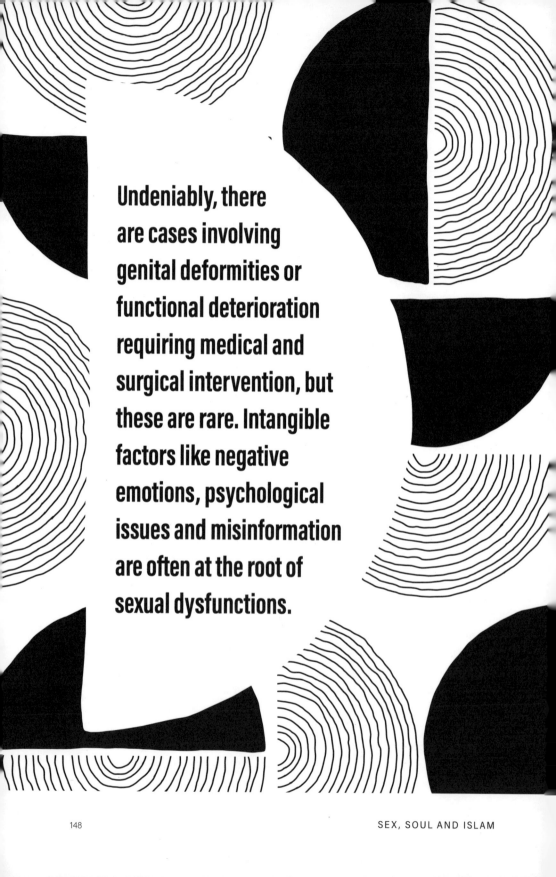

Undeniably, there are cases involving genital deformities or functional deterioration requiring medical and surgical intervention, but these are rare. Intangible factors like negative emotions, psychological issues and misinformation are often at the root of sexual dysfunctions.

all. Hence, the possibility of stimulation is increased due to this aroused state. In addition to this, coital positions, as popularised by the *Kama Sutra*, cause the penis to interface with the clitoris at a variety of angles, depths, pressures and contact points. These intensify, speed up, sustain or delay clitoral and penile stimulation during intercourse for a couple to achieve mutual orgasm. In the end, female orgasm always come back to the clitoris.

The common mistake in understanding female orgasm is conflating the reproductive with the orgasmic processes of sex, as is the reality of male orgasm. With men, the penis plays both functions, whereas with women, the vagina plays a reproductive function while the clitoris is solely for pleasure. Ignorance of this fact has led to many couples chasing female orgasm through vaginal stimulation, failing and then settling for token sex. There are also those who understand the role of the clitoris in orgasm but wrongly insist on partner masturbation or cunnilingus as the best way to satisfy women.[101] As discussed earlier in this chapter, targeting a particular female organ to bring on her orgasm has the potential to alienate women in bed, in turn affecting their arousal. The better lover allows his wife to lead him on what, where and when to target, using sexual knowledge, techniques and skills to stimulate pleasure, but never as a tactic of inducing a quick arousal.

Men Always Want Sex

This myth is based on an established truth that men's physiological cycle, from erection to orgasm, can happen even in the absence of his desire, but this is not the whole truth. There is a limit to a man's capability and it is not necessarily due to any physiological problem on his part. In rare cases, a man's state of mind can ruin his libido, just like in women and we have encountered such cases in counselling. They often involve physically fit and attractive men and women, usually in their mid-thirties. Although the husband is struggling to perform for his wife, the wife will somehow know that her husband is not encountering the same problem in other circumstances, be it through masturbation, watching pornography or with another woman. A third party is the favourite suspect among wives even if in most cases there is no one and even when there is, it is often in the aftermath of their broken relationship rather than the cause of his selective erectile dysfunction. All the same, a non-performing penis is such an indictment on her attractiveness as much as his manhood that it invariably leads to a two-way blame-game.

The real cause has nothing to do with third-party involvement, his impotence or her dwindling attractiveness, or even black magic as was suspected in one case we dealt with. Instead, it is similar to the scenario of the wife who cannot make her husband happy when she is unhappy. The only difference with men is that the effect is not immediately felt in the bedroom. Generally, seeing his wife's body, especially her privates, and receiving sexual stimulation, can bring on his erection even if there are wider problems in the marriage. But as always, everything has its limits. If the relationship continues to deteriorate, a man can be so emotionally affected that his supposedly unfailing physiological automations cannot surmount it. One example we came across was an unemployed husband who was routinely belittled by his working wife, sometimes in the presence of others. His financial incapacitation and her disdain towards his inability to provide combined to completely demolish his long-held self-image as her consummate provider and therefore, his body could no longer perform like it could when he fulfilled the role of breadwinner.

While the myth of a man being continually "up for it" prevails, cases of male sexual reticence will always be viewed negatively as something suspect or unnatural, but with the myth dispelled, a husband's sexual fastidiousness can actually be seen as a good thing because a man whose physiological cycle is more dependent on his psycho-emotions is nearer to his wife in terms of sexual perception. Couples who can close their gender gap in sexual perception will inevitably be better equipped to incorporate the five senses, emotional intimacy and imagination into their sex life, resulting in an enhanced sexual experience for both.

The Great Size Debate

The question, "Does size matter?" has dominated discussions on sex for decades. On one online men's magazine, a writer asserts, "We have heard the old saying, it is not the size that matters. It's a lie. Many women want a man with a larger girth. Most men want the bragging rights of having the largest penis in the locker room."[102] And they are not even selling penis enlargement products! The source is a website offering well-meaning advice to men on style, skills and culture. The idea that a large penis is crucial to good sex is also promoted on women's websites, "Ever wondered what could be worse than getting a root canal? Well, how about waiting months upon months to have sex with a guy and you find out he has a small ding-dong. Imagine starving for food and you look in the refrigerator, only to find there is nothing to munch on."[103]

Another female writer contradicts this view, saying, "A guy with a smaller penis is more attractive than a guy with a bigger penis who needs you to be all in awe of what he thinks is some cosmic accomplishment but really is just genes or biology or whatever."[104] Despite the difference in opinions, all are examples of our obsession with the size of male genitalia.

In 1978, Dr Bernie Zilbergeld published a study on women's perception of a great lover. The most frequent responses were: tenderness, affection, respect, sensuality

SEX, SOUL AND ISLAM

and kindness. Not one answer mentioned penis size.[105] In 1980, Michael Castleman quoted this work and contrasted it with "men who read the men's magazines" who "learn month after month how important penis size is in lovemaking", and with other observations concluded that, "... most women are not all that concerned about a man's penis size. They want companions, not just penises; men they feel close to, not simply silent organs – even big blood-gorged organs ... Men, not women, criticize penises."[106]

Sexual therapists had long maintained that penis size was a preoccupation of men, along with their misplaced apprehensions on erections, whereas women were more concerned with the overall experience of intimacy, romance and all-encompassing pleasures. However, it seems that women have now jumped on the bandwagon, with thousands of online articles and women's publications insisting that, "penis size matters".[107]

The problem is when men try to keep up with unrealistic notions of what is important in sex, thereby affecting their own performance. In *He Comes Next – The Thinking Woman's Guide to Pleasuring a Man* Dr Kerner explains a phenomenon referred to by some sex therapists as "'spectatoring'", as, "a process in which a person watches his or her own engagement in the sexual event, rather than being fully immersed in the moment itself." He adds, "Some therapists believe that spectatoring is the primary cause of most sexual dysfunction in men."[108] In other words, the anxiety men feel in trying to measure up to an unrealistic expectation about sex is negatively impacting their ability to perform.

To get to the truth, we must differentiate between perception and fact. Much of the debate is about perception or what men think and what women think. Even if some testimonies are based on true experience, it is only as good as what they think they are experiencing. For example, we have just discussed the cases of women mistaking different types of clitoral orgasm for climax through the vagina or G-spot. Similarly, with arguments over penis size, the biological fact does not vary, regardless of differences in what men and women think they have experienced.

In their book *Why Men Don't Have a Clue and Women Always Need More Shoes!* Allan and Barbara Pease present a biological fact which negates all notions that size matters. The average erect penis is 5½ inches long whereas the average vaginal depth is 3½ inches. Incidentally, the vagina stretches and can accommodate various penis sizes. More relevantly here, the erotic regions of the vagina only exist between the opening and halfway down its canal,[109] with the clitoris being the real erotic agent as discussed earlier. Hence, as far as orgasm goes, a man needs much less of his penis than he has.[110] This shows that the importance of size is more for procreative rather than pleasuring purposes. There is no denying that size may have some psychological effects like inspiring confidence in a man or as a symbol of arousing masculinity for a woman, but this should be viewed as a bonus rather than a necessity. It makes no sense to fret about penis size as it only increases anxiety which can affect performance. In reality, as far as organs go, the most important one for good sex is the brain.

Pornography Can Improve Sex

In one of our "Sex and Intimacy" classes, included as part of a marriage preparation course, a participant made a spirited and well-meaning suggestion that they all ought to watch pornography to learn about sex before their wedding because otherwise they would not have any prior exposure to it as non-marital sex is strictly forbidden in Islam. There is a certain logic going on there. In fact, others have stretched that logic to argue that married couples can also enrich their sexual repertoire by watching porn. On the contrary, many sex-therapists believe porn-watching can lead to sexual dysfunctions.[111] We shall use an analogy to simplify their explanations:

Trying to be good at sex by watching pornography is like trying to be good at Kung-Fu by watching Jackie Chan or Bruce Lee films. Most of us understand that it takes decades of discipleship to develop the necessary strength, skills, knowledge, confidence and temperament to become a Kung-Fu master. We also recognise that whatever abilities such martial arts stars do have are exaggerated on-screen. Somehow, we know that this approach to learning martial arts is not workable or realistic and can potentially lead to long-term injury.

A mutually satisfying sexual encounter requires understanding and empathy between the partners as to each other's erogenous zones, likes and dislikes, repertoire of skills, comfort level, sense of timing and appetite for adventure. To reach such an understanding takes years of experimentation and communication and maintaining it is a deliberate, ongoing effort. Yet, many porn-watchers actually believe they can emulate the kind of sex they see on screen, even as they recognise back-flipping, mid-air stunts they witness in a Kung-Fu film should not be attempted by amateurs in real life. If only people could apply their common sense when looking to pornography for sexual guidance. Just like other sectors of show-business, the porn industry's main objective is not the dissemination of accurate information on sex, but the acquirement of profit.

In this way, porn perpetuates sexual misinformation on two levels: exceptional endowment and sheer fantasy. The first is what the industry looks for in their actors: the tallest, prettiest, biggest, longest, tautest, the sexual hyperbole they know will make them money. Admittedly, these exceptionally endowed human-beings do

There is **no valid** reason for not prioritising the human body in the scheme of **Islamic** development. Considering it **vain** or shallow is false piety as the Islamic teachings are replete with commandments to **look after** our bodies through **eating** well, restraining desires, eschewing luxuries and being **physically** active.

exist, but they do not represent the majority of humanity nor are their superhuman assets essential to great sex. This is of no concern in the world of pornography because it is about what sells, not what is true. This brings us to the second way in which the industry perpetuates myths. Through presenting fantastical ideas of sex as reality. In such a make-believe world, there is no liability. Here, every manoeuvre will bring on those body-writhing pangs of erotic pleasure almost instantaneously – from men and women alike. The psycho-emotional readiness, sensual pleasuring and two-way communication needed for good lovemaking in the real world do not exist in porn films. As Michael Castleman puts it:

> From a perspective of problem-free lovemaking, the most glaring sex education error in pornography is the absence of leisurely whole-body sensuality. Hardcore media fixate on the sexual and exclude anything the least bit playful or sensual. Except for generally brief and never tender attention to women's breasts, the focus is almost entirely genital, which reinforces many men's view that lovemaking is all genital ... It is the logical conclusion of the "wham, bam, thank you ma'am" lovestyle ... Unlike most lovers, the actors in pornography appear perpetually aroused. The women are always eager to get down or go down. And the men boast not only enormous penises that inspire penis envy in the average man, but instant ever-hard erections as well ... A man who expects himself to measure up to the speed of arousal or penis size in pornography usually concludes that he must be a woefully inadequate lover. The stress engendered by the "failure" can contribute to sex problems."

(Michael Castleman)[112]

This was published in 1980 when sex magazines and videos were the extent of pornographic material and had to be bought in person. Today, the internet makes a wide variety of explicit and degrading images and films accessible from the comfort of our living rooms and smartphones. The proliferation of internet porn combines with the condition called 'spectatoring' to give rise to a new syndrome termed by Dr Kerner as "Sexual Attention Deficit Disorder" (SADD):

> ... Guys with SADD have become so accustomed to the high levels of visual novelty and stimulation that comes from internet porn that they're unable to focus on real sex with a real woman. As a result, guys with SADD often find it difficult to maintain an erection during intercourse, or

SEX, SOUL AND ISLAM

they experience delayed ejaculation and can only climax with manual or
oral stimulation." [113]

Unfortunately, the consumption of pornography is an issue in the Muslim community as well. We have come across wives who have caught their husbands literally, with their pants down, watching porn. Granted, since these marriages were already on the rocks, it would not be fair to blame it all on the adult film industry. But one particular case proved how detrimental porn consumption can be to a marriage. A practising wife who was otherwise happy with her practising husband, was disgusted by him showing her a viral "secret video" of their favourite artiste couple in a split-bamboo manoeuvre, suggesting they try to emulate it. It became an issue when the husband started taunting the wife with labels like prude and frigid for her refusal to participate.

The marriage was not otherwise dysfunctional and the husband was not using porn as a coping mechanism for sex deprivation. Rather, it was his attempt at enriching their sex-life. Both knew it is *haram* or forbidden in Islam, but the normalcy with which the video was being circulated and discussed among the husband's work colleagues had mitigated his sense of wrong-doing. In addition, his unhappiness at her refusal also betrayed a common trait of neglect concerning female desire which is that it should be as easily stoked with sensory stimulation as male desire is. Given the fact that sex education is largely taboo in Muslim societies today, the sexual misinformation disseminated through pornography can contribute significantly to the gender-gap of sexual perception – which has a negative impact on sexual satisfaction in Muslim marriages.

Muslim couples must first remember that watching pornography is forbidden in Islam, most importantly because it involves watching other people's *aurah* or nakedness. This is for very good reasons. The reality defies the touted logic that watching others having sex can improve our own sex life. Factors like exceptional physique and capability, the extremes of every sexual scenario and the addictive effect of explicit images combine to perpetuate unrealistically high sexual expectations through the consumption of false depiction and misinformation concerning the sexual process. Instead of enhancing, all of these are detrimental to the mutually shared sexual experience. Even if your intention is sincere and directed at enhancing your marriage, the Islamic message is clear and should not be ignored. In Islam, "the ends do not justify the means", especially if the means are known to be *haram*.

There will always be those partners who claim they can differentiate the reality from the distortion and guard themselves against addiction, in which case the prohibition must not apply to them. It is the same rhetoric used to justify social drinking and social gambling: we know the limits and have self-control. Whether or not such claims are true only Allah ﷻ knows. Nobody else has the right to judge, but the law is another matter. As far as the law is concerned, it applies to everyone who believes in the wisdom of Allah ﷻ who knew the limits of mankind when He created them. All believers must be wary of seeing themselves as above God's Laws.

Conclusion

In this chapter, we have covered the basic similarities and differences between the male and female sexual experiences, the "messenger" hadith which works to close this gender-gap via the sensual and social dimensions of lovemaking, how this outlook on sex can be sustained throughout marriage and how sexual myths can propagate a culture which is at odds with this outlook.

This is only the beginning. Intimacy is not static. It can grow or wither away. Marriage does not guarantee that romance will bloom forever. To keep it alive, we must make the intention to learn new things, hone new skills and explore new ideas. We cannot be complacent. A very good place to start is sensual and erotic massage. It is a skill that can realistically be learnt and a good introduction to extended sensuality. Self-help sex-enrichment books written by experienced sex therapists can give ideas on healthy ways to reintroduce romance to a marriage. The academically inclined may delve into sexual research to understand the inner workings of sex, recognise when there are problems and use that understanding to enrich their sex-life. Wherever available, sex enrichment workshops are also great learning opportunities for couples who want to enhance their understanding of sex and share ideas with experts and peers alike.

Unfortunately, there is a distinct lack of scientific research conducted by Muslims on the topic of sex. Likewise, sexual relationship books or enrichment workshops taught from an Islamic perspective, are few and far between. However, Muslim couples should embrace multiple sources of knowledge and learn to separate acceptable content from that which espouses moral values contradictory to Islamic teachings, but we must also refer to authoritative Islamic publications providing sexual values, ethics and rulings to act as our guide. Above all, the most important source of understanding and discovery must be our life partners. Hence, the journey towards the mutual bliss, mercy and tranquillity of true marital intimacy, must be made together.

SEX, SOUL AND ISLAM

EPILOGUE

Central to the Islamic story of life is the encounter between two diametrically opposite elements of the human being: sex and soul. The soul's journey, from non-existence towards its eternal destiny in the Hereafter, passes through this Earthly realm of matter, alien to its own nature. It's residence here, namely the human body, is as material as the Earth it sits upon and it is in this bodily home that soul meets sex.

The carnal, animalistic pleasures of sex lure the body into its perpetual cycle of procreation to house the multitude of passing souls. If it were not for Allah's promised guidance, these pleasures could just as well tempt the souls into the immediate but temporal allure of Earthly bliss, away from the path they are supposed to seek, towards the eternal and everlasting bliss of the Hereafter. Islam reveals the true nature of sex and its place in the cycle of life on Earth. It shows the human a transcendent facet of the sexual experience, a sampling of the real Paradise, as well as the potential to cultivate a garden on Earth where new seeds can be sown and young souls can be nurtured.

The way to the transcendent is clarified by Allah's Messenger ﷺ who guides us to elevate ourselves above the perfunctory sex of other animals through emotional and sensual pleasuring, opening the door to the full array of human intimacies. In that way, sex ceases from being a threat to our souls, instead becoming an ally. Sex and soul unite in their shared experience of the human condition and only then can the act of mating lead to the Quranic ideal of tranquillity, love and mercy.

However, all too often the Prophetic way to this Quranic ideal is obscured from Muslims' own view due to our selective emphasis on one aspect of Islamic guidance, namely the law. To make matters worse, somehow, the male-serving interpretations of these laws prevailed in much of Muslim societies and Islamic history. But the Quranic ideal can be reclaimed, if we embrace the Prophetic insights and guidance on lovemaking holistically.

It begins with internalising our faith in the procreational, familial and social roles of lovemaking in establishing conducive environments for the cultivation of souls, culminating in a commitment to the Islamic culture of sexual purity within the exclusive zone called marriage. This faith would then become a rudder that steers the observance of marital laws towards mutual bliss and no longer be an instrument of dominance, coercion, selfishness, ill-treatment and abuse of conjugal rights. When couples are united in thinking and approach towards sex, they stand a better chance of taming the carnality of sex, letting the fuller spectrum of pleasures that accompany human lovemaking advocated by the Prophet ﷺ to bond their souls. And this entails a lifetime of mutual nurturing even as they bring in new souls into their little paradise on Earth to nurture them with the same faith, laws and values.

Let's reclaim the Quranic ideal and make that unlikely alliance between sex and soul happen in our own love story by embracing holistically the Prophet's ﷺ guidance on lovemaking so that tranquillity, love and mercy may prevail in our marriages as envisaged in *Al-Rum 30:21:*

> *And of His signs is that He created for you from yourselves mates that you may find tranquillity in them; and He placed between you love and mercy. Indeed in that are signs for a people who give thought.*

SEX, SOUL AND ISLAM

ENDNOTES

1   Other than marriage, the Quran refers to another institution which allows for a sexual relationship with "those whom your right hand possesses". This refers to captives of war. Why slavery is not lawful to Muslims today is explained in the footnotes of Chapter Two. There is also a concept of temporary marriage known as *mut'ah* of which *sunni* and *shia* scholars would differ in its legal status. Since marriage is the universally recognised institution to regulate sexual relationships among Muslims today, we limit the discussions to marriage only, despite the existence of these alternatives.

2   E. A. Hoebel and E. L. Frost, *Cultural and social anthropology*, TMH edition, Tata Mc-Graw-Hill, 1979; p. 6

3   E. A. Hoebel and E. L. Frost, *Cultural and social anthropology*, TMH edition; p. 168

4   M. Ghazali, *Ihya Ulumuddin, Book III*, Book Lovers Bureau, Lahore, n.d.; p. 102

5   E. Fromm, *The Art of Loving*, Harper Perennial Modern Classics, 1956; p. 24

6   E. Fromm, *The Art of Loving*; p. 25

7   J. Nurbakhsh, *Sufi Women*, Khaniqahi-Nimatullahi Publications, 1990; p. 62

8   M. Ghazali, *Ihya Ulumuddin;* Volume IV, Chapter 6 "Love and Attachment"; p. 297

9   A. Y. Ali, *The Holy Quran - Text, Translation and Commentary*, The Muslim Converts' Association of Singapore; p. 939, footnote 3114.

10   A. Bouhdiba, *Sexuality in Islam*, Rouledge and Kegan Paul, 1985; pp. 194 – 195: ... the sexual life of the young Arabo-Muslim is very often ... taken over by organised prostitution, whether public or not ... In a society that exalts desire and, at the same time, impedes it, only the prostitute can transcend taboos, violate prohibitions and satisfy it ... The role of the prostitute is to appease tensions.

11   A. Bouhdiba, *Sexuality in Islam;* p. 200: The meeting of the sexes are ... so jealously guarded to the minimum that there was a constant temptation to violate them. Thus homosexual relations are relatively encouraged in Arabo-Muslim societies, to the detriment of intersexual relations ... It is difficult for those who have not ex-perienced it to imagine what life under a strict separation of the sexes is like. But it is understandable that homosexuality, so violently condemned by Islam, could be so widely practised by both men and women.

12   This is not to criticise present-day hijab-related rulings like compulsory head covering rules in Iran and Saudi Arabia or close proximity *(khalwats)* rules in Malaysia. There is a case for and against such rulings, but that is for another book. Here, suffice to say that the first generation of Muslims observed the *hijab* code voluntarily.

13   Refer to note #1. We refer to the offence as non-marital sex here as it is the most relevant in our day and age.

14   E. A. Hoebel, *Cultural and social anthropology*; p. 169

15   R. L. Beals and H. Hoijer, *An introduction to Anthropology*, Macmillan Publishing, 1977; pp. 379 & 380

16   J. Poshter, Fact Tank, Pew Research Centre website, 15 April 2014: What's morally acceptable? It depends on where in the world you live; Key takeaway #3: 46% across the 40 nations saw sex between unmarried adults as morally unacceptable.

      Source: https://www.pewresearch.org/fact-tank/2014/04/15/whats-morally-acceptable-it-depends-on-where-in-the-world-you-live/

17   A. Muhammad Fazl-ur-Rahman. *The Quranic Foundations and Structure of Muslim Society,* Volume I. Islamic Book Trust, 2001; p. 300: The Holy Quran affirms … the existence of two aspects of human nature, namely, an-Nafs al-Ammarah (the Impelling or Carnal Self)* and an-Nafs al-Lawwamah (the Reproaching or Moral Self)** and of the conflict between them. Moreover, it affirms that this situation of conflict has to be resolved through discarding the behests of the Carnal Self at the instance of the Moral Self; thereby enabling the self to be transformed into al-Nafs al-Mutmainnah (the Self-at-Peace, or, the Beatified Self) [Footnote: *XII:53 ** LXXV:2 ***LXXIX:27 referring to Quranic references].

18   R. Tannahill, *Sex in History*, Abacus, 1992; p. 233

19   R. Tannahill, *Sex in History*; p. 227

20   R. Tannahill, *Sex in History*; p. 225 – Although Tannahill used these exact words to describe Byzantine women, she had earlier explained that such customs were adopted by Muslims invading the frontiers of Byzantium.

21   R. Tannahill, *Sex in History*; p. 229

22   R. Tannahill, *Sex in History*; p. 223

23   A. Bouhdiba, *Sexuality in Islam.* Rouledge and Kegan Paul, 1985; p. 112

24   A. Bouhdiba, *Sexuality in Islam*; p. 115

25   A. Bouhdiba, Sexuality in Islam; p. 104

26   A. Bouhdiba, *Sexuality in Islam*; p. 91

27   A. Bouhdiba, *Sexuality in Islam*; p. 116

28   A. Bouhdiba, *Sexuality in Islam*; p. 160

29   A. Bouhdiba, *Sexuality in Islam*; p. 230

30   A. Bouhdiba, *Sexuality in Islam*; p. 109

31   H. Hazlin "Obedient Wives shrug off Criticism", *The Straits Times* [Singapore], 19 June 2011, p. 14

32   J. Greenberg, *Sexuality – Insights and Issues*, Brown and Benchmark Publishers, 1992; pp. 29 – 30

33   M. Hughes and J. Taylor, Rape 'impossible' in marriage, says Muslim cleric, 23 October 2011: Where in Sheikh Maulana Abu Sayeed, President of the Islamic Sharia Council in Britain and Inayat Bunglawala, Chairman of Muslims4UK, had opposing views regarding the criminality of marital rape in Islam.

34   "Anas reported that the Messenger of Allah 🌺 had a Persian neighbour who could prepare a good soup. One day he cooked soup for the Messenger of Allah 🌺 and came to him to invite him. The Messenger of Allah asked: 'And is 'Aishah invited too?' He replied; 'No.' So the Messenger of Allah 🌺 said: 'No, (in declining the invitation).' The neighbour returned once more and invited him again and the Messenger of Allah 🌺 asked; 'Is 'A'ishah invited too?' He replied; 'No', and so the Messenger of Allah 🌺 said; 'No (in declining the invitation).' He returned a third time to invite him and Allah's Messenger 🌺 again asked: 'And is 'Aishah invited too?' the neighbour replied; 'Yes', so the Prophet and 'Ā'ishah made their way until they reached his house." (Muslim)

35   A. Bouhdiba, *Sexuality in Islam*; p.89: According to another tradition the Prophet 🌺 cursed the *maswwifa* and the *mughallisa* woman. The first is the woman who, when invited by her husband to make love, always replies *saufa* (not just yet). The second is the woman who falsely claims to be having her period. (Quoting from a a full commentary by *Aini, Umdatul Qari fi Sharh al-Bukhari*, Istanbul, 1308h, 11 volumes)

Authors' note: We didn't find the hadith used by Bouhdiba in Bukhari's collection but in Ibn Hibban's, wherein it was classified as *dhaif* or weak. We use Bouhdiba' reference to it not as basis for our main argument but only as a possible explanation for the existence of the women-specific hadiths.

36   B. Liz, "'He's permitted to hit her': Alarming video appears to condone domestic violence", *Sky News*, 14 April 2017.

Source: www.news.com.au/lifestyle/relationships/marriage/hes-permitted-to-hit-her-alarming-video-appears-to-condone-domestic-violence/news-story/f6f-517cac59eccad98e0768d4604feb0

37   "If it were not for the fear of retaliation on the Day of Resurrection, I would have beaten you with this miswak (tooth-cleaning twig)." (Ibn Majah)

38   This refers to the Jahiliyah practice of forceful inheritance of widows upon the death of their husband and it is prohibited in verse Al-Nisa 4:19

39   As a teenager, Osman Sidek attended the late ustaz's weekly morning classes in the now-demolished Singapore village of Kampong Pachitan in the 1970s. Wife beating was one of the numerous current issues the ustaz addressed in these classes.

40   Very much like wife-beating, guidance on the practice of slavery found in the Quran, Sunna and Islamic jurisprudence should not be misconstrued as Islam condoning or encouraging slavery. Islam is ideologically against slavery calling mankind to submit to no one other than God Almighty, but its abolishment would take longer than the Prophet Muhammad's 🌺 lifetime through a necessarily gradual process

involving legal and moral codes enjoining humane treatment of slaves and incentivising manumission; instead of unproductively dismantling the only means feasible then for containing defeated enemy fighters.

Today, all Muslim countries in the world are signatories of international anti-slavery conventions stipulating it as illegal. Due to that, Islamic justifications by Boko Haram and ISIS for their sexual enslavement atrocities are actually invalid as verse Al-Isra 17:34 demands that Muslims fulfil all covenants we undertake.

41   S. Hite, *The Hite Report – A Nationwide Study of Female Sexuality*, Dell Publishing, 1981; pp. 451 - 477

42   Again, such general statements were made in the presence of men. But its meaning is applicable to women as well.

43   H.-ur-Rahman al'Azmi, *Musannaf ibn Abi Shayba* (Arabic), (3/401), Sharikat Dar al-Qibla & Mu'assasah Ulum al-Quran, 1040H

44   "When you marry a woman or buy a slave-girl, take her by the forelock and ask for baraka ..." (Malik)

45   S. Sabiq, *Fikih Sunna*, Translated by Mahyuddin Syaf, Al-Azhar, 1987; p. 139

46   S. Sabiq, *Fikih Sunna,* Translated by Mahyuddin Syaf, Al-Azhar, 1987; pp. 137 – 138

47   S. Sabiq, *Fikih Sunna,* Translated by Mahyuddin Syaf, Al-Azhar, 1987; pp. 137 – 138

48   S. Hite, *The Hite Report – A Nationwide Study of Female Sexuality,* Dell Publishing, 1981; pp. 356-357

     Our note: In no way are we suggesting that this is common. Hite too commented that "These were very unusual answers" concerning the 12 respondents who reported self-stimulating themselves towards orgam during penetrative sex in her study on "Orgasm from clitoral stimulation by hand".

49   "... Hence 'Urwah said (concerning Prophet Muhammad's ﷺ followers): '... I definitely see a collection of people well-advised to flee and leave you.' Abu Bakar ﷺ said to him: 'Go suck the clitoris of al-Lat, are we going to flee and leave him? ...'" (Bukhari)

50   Even though only one volume is published in English, the complete set of five volumes was published in this Arabic publication:
كتاب الفقه على المذاهب الاربعة، الشيخ عبد الرحمان الجزيري، دار الكتاي العلمية، بيروت، لبنان، 1360 هـ.

51   "Islam's Stance on Oral Sex", *Islamawareness,* 19 May 2004.

     Source: www.islamawareness.net/Sex/fatwa_sex_001.html

52   إتحاف السـادة المتقين بـشرح إحيـاء علوم الديـن، السـيد محمـد الحسـيني الزبيـدي، الجـزء الخامس، طبـع مؤسسـة التريـخ العربيـة، 1994م، صفحـة 372: (وليقدم) قبـل الجـماع بمقدماته وهـي (التلطف بالـكلام والتقبيـل) في الخديـن والشـفة ودغدغـة الثـدى والحالـب والغمـز في أطـراف البطـن والخـاصر

     S. Muhamad al Husaini al Zabidi, *Ittihaf asSaadat ulMuttaqin with commentary of Ihya 'Ulumuddin*, Part five, Arabic History Foundation, 1994; p. 372: "And approach intercourse with its preambles which is seducing with words and kissing on the cheeks and the lips to titillate the breasts and nipples and to stimulate every part of the body and loins".

53   S. Jakhura, "Fatwa – Oral Sex", *Darul Ihsan Islamic Services Centre,* 30 July 2016.

Source: www.darulihsan.com/index.php/q-a/fatwa-q-a/nikah-marriage/item/3386-fatwa-oral-sex

54   H. LeWine, "HPV transmission During Oral Sex a Growing Cause of Mouth and Throat Cancer", *Harvard Health Publications,* 29 November 2016.

Source: www.health.harvard.edu/blog/hpv-transmission-during-oral-sex-a-growing-cause-of-mouth-and-throat-cancer-201306046346

N. Hinde, "HPV Through Oral Sex Could Become 'Leading Cause of Mouth Cancer', Experts Predict." *Huffpost,* 16 November 2015.

Source: https://www.huffingtonpost.co.uk/2015/11/16/can-oral-sex-cause-mouth-cancer_n_8573164.html?utm_campaign=share_twitter&ncid=engmodushpmg00000004

K. Mccrum, "Unprotected Oral Sex 'Has Become the Leading Cause of Mouth Cancer'", *Mirror,* 15 November 2015.

Source: www.mirror.co.uk/news/world-news/unprotected-oral-sex-has-become-6855939

55   S. Johnson, "Vaginal Yeast Infection", *Healthline*, 4 October 2016.

Source: www.healthline.com/health/vaginal-yeast-infection

56   D. Renshaw, *Seven Weeks to Better Sex*, Random House, 1995; p. 48: "A vibrator can provide a more intense sexual response and a quicker climax then manual masturbation because it stimulates the rich vibratory nerve endings that cluster at the base of the penis or clitoris."

57   Of course, this exclude circumstances like punishment for crime, war, self-defence or even emergency life-saving surgery in the absence of anesthetics and the like, but even in such cases, bodily harm is always taken as the last resort when no other alternative is available. The same cannot be said of sex.

58   D. Toolbox, "6 Myths about BDSM Inspired by "50 Shades of Grey", *Divine Caroline,* n.d. 2012, www.divinecaroline.com/love-sex/6-myths-about-bdsm-inspired-50-shades-grey.

59   W. Master and V. Johnson, *Human Sexual Response,* Little, Brown, 1966.

60   J. Greenberg, C. Bruess and K. Mullen, *Sexuality – Insights and Issues,* Brown and Benchmark Publishers, 1992; p. 299

61   S. Hite, *The Hite Report – A Nationwide Study of Female Sexuality*, Dell Publishing, 1981; pp. 315 - 386

62   J. Greenberg, C. Bruess and K. Mullen, *Sexuality – Insights and Issues*; p. 126

63   J. Greenberg, C. Bruess and K. Mullen, *Sexuality – Insights and Issues*; p. 126

64   I. Kerner, *He Comes Next – The Thinking Woman's Guide to Pleasuring a Man*. Regan Books, 2006; p. 31

65   S. Hite, *The Hite Report – A Nationwide Study of Female Sexuality*; p. 333

66   S. Hite, *The Hite Report – A Nationwide Study of Female Sexuality*; p. 333

67   J. Bindel, Shere Hite Obituary, 15 Sep 2020: She was catapulted to fame by her groundbreaking study into female sexual response, *The Hite Report: A Nationwide Study of Female Sexuality,* published in 1976,

        Source: https://www.theguardian.com/society/2020/sep/15/shere-hite-obituary

68   S. Hite, *The Hite Report – A Nationwide Study of Female Sexuality*; p. 339

69   K. Lette, *The Straits Times,* Singapore, 2 Oct 2015.

70   S. Hite, *The Hite Report – A Nationwide Study of Female Sexuality*; p. 343

71   M. S. Rizvi, *Marriage and Morals in Islam,* Vancouver Islamic Educational Foundation, 1990; p. 85

72   Samaha, "Let my heart be my veil", *Americanistan,* 30 November 2006, www.americanistan.com/id24.html

        (Our note: Unfortunately we could not track down this poetry in the original language to throw light on the exact meaning of Rumi's words. An English reader may find the idea of dominating or being dominated a bit of a narrow interpretation of the dynamics of passsion. But Eastern languages are rich with shades of meaning and it is very likely that the original word would carry positive and negative connotations of domination which we have interpreted as "mesmerise" and "subjugate and oppress" in the paragraph before this quotation)

73   M. Ghazali, *Ihya Ulumuddin, Book III*; p. 102

74   I. Kerner, *He Comes Next – The Thinking Woman's Guide to Pleasuring a Man,* Harper Collins Publishing, 2004; p. 100

        "Foreplay", *Dictionary.com,* Random House Inc., 2016, www.dictionary.com/browse/foreplay

75   M. Castleman, *Sexual Solutions – A Guide for Men and the Women Who Love Them,* Touchstone, 1980; p. 61

76   I. Kerner, *He Comes Next – The Thinking Woman's Guide to Pleasuring a Man* p. 100

77   D. Renshaw, *Seven Weeks to Better Sex*; p. 91

78   M. Castleman, *Sexual Solutions – A Guide for Men and the Women Who Love Them*; p. 62

79   A. Pease and B. Pease, *Why Men Don't Have a Clue and Women Always Need More Shoes!,* Pease International, 2005; p. 253

80   D. Renshaw, *Seven Weeks to Better Sex;* p. 82

        M. Castleman, *Sexual Solutions – A Guide for Men and the Women Who Love Them*; p. 72

81   D. Renshaw, *Seven Weeks to Better Sex;* p. 53

82   D. Renshaw, *Seven Weeks to Better Sex*; p. 85

83   M. Castleman, *Sexual Solutions – A Guide for Men and the Women Who Love Them;* pp. 166-172

84   M. Castleman, *Sexual Solutions – A Guide for Men and the Women Who Love Them;* p. 38

85   M. Castleman, *Sexual Solutions – A Guide for Men and the Women Who Love Them;* p. 73

86   M. Castleman, *Sexual Solutions – A Guide for Men and the Women Who Love Them;* pp. 84 - 87

87   M. Castleman, *Sexual Solutions – A Guide for Men and the Women Who Love Them;* p. 48 for Victorianism.

        Renshaw, *Seven Weeks to Better Sex;* p. 77 for Inability to Achieve Orgasm.

88   D. Renshaw, *Seven Weeks to Better Sex;* p. xiv

89   M. Castleman, *Sexual Solutions – A Guide for Men and the Women Who Love Them;* p. 172

90   P. Scott, *Sensual Massage,* Ryland Peters and Small, 2006; pp. 15-16

91   B. Amaar. "Report: Muslim countries among world's most obese." *Ummah Sports: The Intersection of Sports & Islam,* 21 Nov. 2014, www.ummahsports.net/2014/11/21/report-muslim-countries-among-worlds-most-obese.

92   I. Kerner, *He Comes Next – The Thinking Woman's Guide to Pleasuring a Man;* p. 34

93   S. Hite, *The Hite Report – A Nationwide Study of Female Sexuality;* p. 229: "Did most of the women in this study orgasm regularly during intercourse ... No. It was found that only approximately 30 percent of the women in this study could orgasm regularly from intercourse."

        D. Renshaw, *Seven Weeks to Better Sex,* p. 39: "Only 20 to 30 percent of women can have coital climax – that is orgasm during intercourse."

94   J. Greenberg, C. Bruess and K. Mullen, *Sexuality – Insights and Issues;* p. 130: Masters and Johnson ... found orgasms from coitus to be less intense than orgasms from non-coital means. These findings were validated by Hite (1976) who found that clitorally stimulated orgasm to be more intense than the orgasm from coitus.

95   J. Greenberg, C. Bruess and K. Mullen, *Sexuality – Insights and Issues;* p. 95

96   J. Greenberg, C. Bruess and K. Mullen, *Sexuality – Insights and Issues;* p. 96: ... a study by Alzate and Londono (1948) could not locate a particular spot such as that described by Grafenberg. Heath (1984) found an area of erotic sensitivity and concluded it is larger than described before ... Women who experience orgasm from the stimulation of the G-spot often report them to be intense.

97   I. Kerner, *She Comes First, A Thinking Man's Guide to Pleasuring a Woman,* Harper Collins Publisher, New York, 2004; p. 22: "In fact, the clitoris was created from the same embryonic tissue as the penis and can be compared point by point with the male genitalia. And unlike the penis – burdened with the responsibilities of reproduction and the removal of waste – the clitoris is devoted solely to pleasure and

confers upon the female "an infinitely greater capacity for sexual response than a man ever dreamed of."

98   I. Kerner, *She Comes First, A Thinking Man's Guide to Pleasuring a Woman;* p. 23: The deep interior walls of the vagina really have few nerve endings and are quite insensitive when stroked or lightly pressed.

99   I. Kerner, *She Comes First, A Thinking Man's Guide to Pleasuring a Woman;* p. 21: There's more to the clitoris than meets the eye … the head is just the tip of the iceberg … the clitoris has three components – a head, a shaft and a base – that extend throughout the pelvic area, with visible structures encompassing the entire area of the vulva, from the top of the pubic bone to the anus, as well as unseen parts inside the vaginal area.

100   I. Kerner, *She Comes First, A Thinking Man's Guide to Pleasuring a Woman;* p. 52: A G-spot orgasm, like all female orgasms, is a clitoral orgasm; its part of the same pleasure network.

       D. Renshaw, *Seven Weeks to Better Sex*; p. 39: "We now know that there is only one type of female orgasm, triggered by the stimulation of the roots of the clitoris, similar to those in the penis, that attach to the front arch of the pelvic bones."

101   As explained in Chapter 3, "cunnilingus" is stimulation of the clitoris using the tongue, lips or other parts of the mouth, also known as oral stimulation or oral sex on women. "Partner masturbation" refers to manual stimulation of the genitals using either the hands, other parts of the body or even stimulatory devices also known as "sex toys".

102   Breakstudios, "How to Make your Penis Bigger Without Visiting the Hospital", *Made Man Gentlemen Welcome,* 16 May 2020 www.mademan.com/mm/how-make-your-penis-bigger-home-remedies.html#ixzz401w207TH

103   T. Oh, "5 Signs He Has a Small One", *I Wish I Knew This: Love, Dating and Everything in Between,* www.iwishiknewthis.com/5-signs-he-may-have-a-small-one

104   C. Stuckton, "Women on 'Does Dick Size Matter.'" *Thought Catalog,* 6 August 2013, www. thoughtcatalog.com/christine-stockton/2013/08/50-women-on-does-dick-size-matter

105   B. Zilberger, *Male Sexuality,* Boston, Little Brown, 1978.

106   M. Castleman, *Sexual Solutions – A Guide for Men and the Women Who Love Them*; p. 32

107   J. Welsh, "Sorry Guys, Penis Size Matters", *Business Insider,* 9 April 2013, www.businessinsider.com/penis-size-matters-in-physical-attractive-ness-2013-4?IR=T&r=US&IR=T

108   I. Kerner, *He Comes Next – The Thinking Woman's Guide to Pleasuring a Man* p. xvii: Sex therapists call this condition "spectatoring" – a process in which a person watches his or her own engagement in the sexual event, rather than being fully immersed in the moment itself … Some therapists believe that spectatoring is the primary cause of most sexual dysfunction in men.

       D. Renshaw, *Seven Weeks to Better Sex*; p. 18: "Many people tell me they tend to "watch" themselves perform during sex instead of relaxing and enjoying the sexual moment. Such "spectatoring" can build anxiety and impede the relaxed physical responses you need for erection or orgasm. Men in particular may experience erection problem because of such performance anxiety."

109   A. Pease and B. Pease, *Why Men Don't Have a Clue and Women Always Need More Shoes!*; p. 250

110   A. Pease and B. Pease, *Why Men Don't Have a Clue and Women Always Need More Shoes!*, p. 46: "... the vast majority of nerve endings that contribute to female pleasure are located on the surface of a woman's vulva and that no penetration whatsoever is required for a woman to be stimulated to orgasm."

111   A. Pease and B. Pease, *Why Men Don't Have a Clue and Women Always Need More Shoes!*; p. xvii: Truth be told, male sexual anxiety is on the rise. This has much to do with the proliferation of porn, especially given its easy access through the Internet and its emergence into mainstream pop-culture ... Now, more than ever, women need to take an active role in this mission to liberate men from their own oppressive high, unrealistic standards. (Also Michael Castleman, below)

112   M. Castleman, *Sexual Solutions – A Guide for Men and the Women Who Love Them*; pp. 195-198

113   I. Kerner, "Too Much Internet Porn: the SADD Effect", *Askmen,* www.askmen.com/dating/love_tip_500/566_too-much-internet-porn-the-sadd-effect.html